PUFFI

PLAYS FO

Imagine the scene: a quie
pavilion with the gentle so   ..ather on willow
in the background . . .

'It's no good, Deidre. I'm batty over you. You've
really hit me for six. My short square legs go all
googly every time I see you. Pitch in with me,
Deidre, and our lives will know no boundaries.'

This is just a snippet from one of Johnny Ball's
hilarious sketches which were originally written
for the television series 'Star Turn' and 'Playaway'. They can be read alone, read aloud with
friends, or even performed in front of an audience.

If you like jokes you'll love this book; it's full of
loony characters in even loonier situations – and
there's the added bonus of a laugh on every line!

Illustrated by Colin West

Johnny Ball
PLAYS FOR
LAUGHS

A PUFFIN BOOK

Puffin Books, Penguin Books Ltd, Harmondsworth, Middlesex, England
Penguin Books, 40 West 23rd Street, New York, New York 10010, U.S.A.
Penguin Books Australia Ltd, Ringwood, Victoria, Australia
Penguin Books Canada Ltd, 2801 John Street, Markham, Ontario, Canada L3R 1B4
Penguin Books (N.Z.) Ltd, 182–190 Wairau Road, Auckland 10, New Zealand

First published 1983

Set in Linotron Baskerville by
Rowland Phototypesetting Ltd, Bury St Edmunds, Suffolk

Made and printed in Great Britain by
Cox and Wyman Ltd, Reading

This book is for the BBC Children's Television department who commissioned me to write these sketches in the first place. My special thanks to Cynthia Felgate, Ann Reay, Peter (Ivor Notion) Charlton, Christine Secombe, Avril Price, Judy Whitfield, John Smith, Albert Barber and, of course, my dear friend, Brian Cant.

CONTENTS

INTRODUCTION

Recently I have been making television programmes like 'Think Again' which have become quite scientific and often rather serious. Although I very much enjoy making these programmes, I really love *comedy* more than anything. Thinking of this reminded me of the comedy sketches I have written for television over the years.

Many were written for programmes like 'Playaway' and 'Star Turn' and were intended purely to make children laugh. However, kids don't really need television to make them laugh; they are experts at making their own fun no matter where they are or what they are doing.

Kids generally love play acting. My kids, Zoe, Nicky and Danny, are always writing short plays to perform for my wife and me and their friends. Most schools and children's organizations have drama clubs or produce concerts at some time of year, but I am not sure that there is much comedy material written with them in mind and for them to perform.

Hence this book – a collection of sketches that can be enjoyed for themselves or read collectively with different people taking the different parts, or learnt, rehearsed and performed at school concerts and fund-raising events.

I have included here and there some thoughts on scenery and costume, but only where necessary. It is really up to you whether you simply read the sketches, or spend weeks on end making scenery and costumes to turn them into major productions.

I just hope that whoever reads this book gets a lot of fun from it as I had a tremendous time writing it.

Johnny Ball

THE
PICCADILLO LION

Original TV cast:

NARRATOR	Bernard Cribbins
IVOR NOTION	Ian Lavender
MR PICCADILLO, RING MASTER FROM LANCASHIRE	Graeme Garden
ZOLA THE GORGON, THE STRONG MAN	John Craven
MADAM KUSS KUSS, QUEEN OF THE KOSSAKS	Louise Jameson
CLAUD YAVESTOV, RUSSIAN LION-TAMER	Michael Cochrane
MADAM PLUMPTIOUS, COCKNEY FAT LADY	Leslie Judd

This sketch was originally written for the 'Star Turn' series on BBC 1. All the Ivor Notion sketches were performed on television as radio sketches with the characters reading their scripts round a microphone. Ivor is a sort of accidental detective who spots the villain through three silly mistakes. You may like to warn your audience beforehand to look out for these mistakes so that they can spot the villain themselves. Each character can wear or hold something to show which role he or she is playing.

NARRATOR: One day, Ivor Notion had a notion to join a circus. It was a strange idea because Ivor didn't get on with animals. He once had a tortoise that attacked him. Anyway, Ivor went out and found a circus, then found the Ring Master and said . . .

IVOR: Excuse me. Are you the Ring Leader?

MR PICCADILLO [*sounding worried*]: Ring Leader? Ring *Master*. Mr Piccadillo. Owner of the Piccadillo circus. Do you want a job?

IVOR: Well . . . er . . .

PICCADILLO: Right. The circus is under way and we're ever so short-staffed. I've got a trapeze artist that is scared of heights, a fire-eater with heartburn and the India Rubber Man has just gone to jail for a long stretch. Now, you stand there. If anyone asks you to give them a hand, give them a hand.

IVOR: Yes, but . . .

NARRATOR: But Mr Piccadillo had disappeared through a curtain and into the circus ring, just as an enormous man in a leopard skin came out.

IVOR: Who are you?

ZOLA [*speaking in a very deep voice*]: I am Zola the Gorgon. Strong Man. I have just torn a telephone directory to pieces and ripped a piano apart with my bare hands.

IVOR: Ooh. You should try to control yourself.

MADAM KUSS KUSS [*to* IVOR *in a Russian accent*]: Hey, boyski. Come hereski.

IVOR: What?

KUSS KUSS: Help me with my cloakski. I am Madam Kuss Kuss, Queen of the Kossaks. You can assistski meski.

IVOR: Don't you talk funny?

KUSS KUSS: I am from Eastern Europe.

IVOR: Oh, Ukraine?

KUSS KUSS: No, my eye is watering. Quick. Getski my horski.

IVOR: Horski?

KUSS KUSS: Of courski. I rideski the horski bare backski.

IVOR: Won't you catch coldski?

CLAUD YAVESTOV [*with a Russian accent*]: The horse is bare back, you idiot.

IVOR: Well, I didn't know. Who said that?

NARRATOR: Ivor turned round to see a surly-looking character dressed in a safari suit and carrying a large leather whip.

CLAUD: I said that. I am the World's Greatest Lion-Tamer, Claud Yavestov. What are you doing here?

IVOR: Mr Piccadillo asked me to stand here and help people.

CLAUD: Help? Help? How can you help? What do you know about animals?

IVOR: Lots. I used to be surrounded by lions and tigers and elephants every day.

CLAUD: You were in the jungle?

IVOR: No, I worked on a roundabout at the fair.

CLAUD: Bah. I cannot stay with this rubbish circus. I will go back to America. There I am famous. It was in America that I went over the Victoria Falls in a barrel.

MADAM PLUMPTIOUS: Get out of it. 'e says that every night. Don't let 'im worry you, deary.

NARRATOR: These sweet words came from the most enormous lady Ivor had ever seen.

PLUMPTIOUS [*puffing herself out*]: I'm Madam Plumptious, ducky. The circus Fat Lady. That's unless I puncture my inflatable frock. Then I gets me crayons out and I'm the Tattooed Lady. That's in between taking the money at the pay desk and doing me fortune telling.

CLAUD: Bah. She is an imposter.

PLUMPTIOUS: Do you mind. I can foretell the future.

CLAUD: O.K. Give me one example.

PLUMPTIOUS: Er . . . tomorrow will be Thursday.

NARRATOR: Any further discussion on the future was cut short by a loud bump and a groan coming from the circus ring. It was followed quickly by an irate Ring Master.

PICCADILLO: Oh, calamity! The World's Tallest Man has got woodworm in one of his stilts. He's fallen off and landed on the camel.

PLUMPTIOUS: Is he hurt?

PICCADILLO: I'll say. He's got a flat hump.

PLUMPTIOUS: Not the camel. Our Tall Man?

PICCADILLO: He's limping very badly. But that's not surprising. He's still wearing one stilt. The thing is, in a minute, he's supposed to be the Human Cannon Ball.

ZOLA: Well, we can't fire him from a cannon now, and where are we going to find someone else of his calibre?

NARRATOR: There was a silence as all the circus people turned to look at Ivor.

IVOR: 'ere. You're not shooting me from no cannon.

PICCADILLO: But you are the only one thin enough to fit down the barrel. Besides, if you don't do it, you'll be fired.

IVOR: But if I do do it, I'll be fired!

CLAUD: Bah. You cowardly custard. There is nothing to be frightened for. I was fired from a cannon twenty-one times to celebrate your Queen Elizabeth's Coronation in 1963.

PLUMPTIOUS: Never mind all that, deary. Here, let me mind your coat and your money.

IVOR: I haven't got any money.

PLUMPTIOUS: That's all right. In a minute, you're going to be loaded. Ha, ha, ha!

NARRATOR: With that, the Strong Man and the Ring Master helped Ivor across the circus ring and into the barrel of the cannon.

IVOR: It's a bit tight in here.

ZOLA: That's so that you come out straight. If you waggle about you might go anywhere.

PICCADILLO: Yes. That would be dangerous. You might hit somebody on the head.

ZOLA: Yes. Now with luck you should land in that net.

IVOR: What if I overshoot?

PICCADILLO: That means you'll have broken the record. Ready? [*Announcing grandly*] Ladies and Gentlemen. The Human Cannon Ball.

[*The cast can create the necessary sound effects with a pop gun, a swanney whistle and a bass drum thump.*]

PICCADILLO: Good heavens! He's sailed right over the net. It's a new world record.

ZOLA: He's gone straight through the bass drum.

PICCADILLO: I can't see that being beaten again.

KUSS KUSS: Hey, youski. Are you all rightski? You missed the netski.

IVOR: It's a good jobski. The speed I was going, if I'd hit the netski, I'd have come out like ten penn'orth of chipskis.

CLAUD: That was very good. Nearly as good as my record set in Berlin when I won a prize of 10,000 German francs.

NARRATOR: And so, thanks to Ivor Notion, the show went on without a hitch, apart from the sword swallower who got hiccups, until it was time for the circus's final act . . .

PICCADILLO: Ladies and Gentlemen. Claud Yavestov and his amazing Lions.

[*Sound effects: growling noises made by cast.*]

ZOLA: There go the lions into the ring. Now where is Claud?

KUSS KUSS: Oh, helpski, helpski!

IVOR: Just calm yourselfski.

KUSS KUSS: It is Claudski. He has disappearedski.

ZOLA [*in a high voice*]: Disappeared? Sorry. [*In a deep voice*] Disappeared? Then who is going to do the lion-taming?

NARRATOR: Once again all eyes turned to . . .

IVOR: Oh, no! I'm not being a lion-tamer until you get tamer lions.

KUSS KUSS: Don't be frightski. Those lions have no teethski.

IVOR: I don't care. They could give me a nasty suckski.

PICCADILLO: Here, here. What's going on? The crowd are waiting for the lion-tamer.

KUSS KUSS: He has vanishedski.

IVOR: Done a bunkski.

PLUMPTIOUS: Oh help! Oh help! We've been robbed. While I've been telling fortunes, somebody has been creeping up behind me and robbin' the till. They've taken all the circus's money.

CLAUD: Robbin' the till? Who could it have been?

IVOR: Well, that's obvious. While you've been wondering what steps to take to tame those lions, the lion-tamer has been taking big steps away from here with the money.

KUSS KUSS: That is not trueski. Look over hereski.

NARRATOR: Quickly they moved over to one of the lions' travelling cages. Inside the cage lay a very sleepy lion and not two yards away from him lay a large leather whip.

KUSS KUSS: Lookski. The cage is unlocked.

PICCADILLO: Of course it's unlocked. Who's going to steal a lion?

PLUMPTIOUS: Oh, look. That's Claud's whip on the floor. That lion has gorn and swallowed Claud.

ZOLA: It's polished off Yavestov.

KUSS KUSS: I feel so sadski.

PICCADILLO: I bet Claud feels a bit down in the mouth.

PLUMPTIOUS: Eek! Look!

NARRATOR: While they were talking, Ivor Notion opened the door and climbed into the cage. Slowly he walked towards the lion, as everyone held their breath.
[*The cast stands rigid. They all hold their breath.*]

NARRATOR: Ivor carefully bent down to pick up the whip, as the lion growled [*growls*]. Immediately, everyone gasped.

CAST: Gasp!

NARRATOR: Ivor steadied himself, then he cracked the whip. The lion leapt straight at Ivor who sidestepped and grabbed the lion by the scruff of the neck. There was a ZZZZip sound as the lion skin zipped open and out fell Claud Yavestov, still clutching the stolen money.

CLAUD: I'm sorry. I only did it as a joke.

IVOR: Stealing is one thing, but lion about it makes it worse.

PICCADILLO: What made you suspect Claud?

NARRATOR: Asked Mr Piccadillo, after the police had taken the lion-tamer away.

IVOR: Well, he was no good as a lion-tamer. He'd have made a better trapeze artist. They're supposed to get caught in the act. As it was he made three rather silly mistakes. [*To audience.*] Do you know what they were?
[*Here you may accept suggestions from the audience and then reveal the mistakes.*] They were:
1. The Victoria Falls are in Africa. The Niagara Falls are in the U.S.A.
2. The coronation of Queen Elizabeth II was in 1953.
3. German currency is in marks not francs.
If you got them all correct, congratulations.

PLUMPTIOUS: Sssssssssssss . . .

IVOR: What's that hissing sound? Don't tell me the snakes have escaped now.

ZOLA: No, it's only the Fat Lady.

PLUMPTIOUS: Yes, I'm just deflating my inflatable frock.

IVOR: Oh . . .

NARRATOR: Said Ivor Notion,

IVOR: What a letdown.

CURTAIN

WILD BILL HICCUP
RIDES AGAIN

Cast of characters:

WILD BILL HICCUP, DRUNKEN SHERIFF
A VERY STRANGE STRANGER

BILL: Howdy, stranger . . . Hic!

STRANGER: Howdy.

BILL: Tell me, Stranger, you're a stranger round these parts, ain't you, Stranger? Hic!

STRANGER: I dunno. I never been here before.

BILL: That ain't strange, coming from a stranger. Hic! What's yer name, Stranger?

STRANGER: Folks call me Tex.

BILL: I guess that's cause you come from Texas. Hic!

STRANGER: Nope. I come from Louisiana but I ain't havin' people call me Louise. Who's the sheriff of this hick town?

BILL: I thought that would have been obvious. Hic! Hiccup's the name. Wild Bill Hiccup, sometimes known as the Bicarbonate Cowboy. I was one of the early settlers. Hic! At the moment, I'm looking for the varmint who robbed the bank yesterday. Hic! He's round here someplace.

STRANGER: Is he dangerous?

BILL: Nope. Hic! He's a safe robber.

STRANGER: Well, I just seen a masked man going into the bank.

BILL: He's O.K. He works there. He's the loan arranger. Hic! He's just been helping me hold up the stage coach.

STRANGER: You and him held up the stage coach?

BILL: We had to. Somebody stole the wheels. Hic!

STRANGER: I don't wish to know that. Kindly leave the stage coach out of this. I want to know if I can drive my cattle through here.

BILL: Drive yer cattle? Hic! What kind of a car is a cattle?

STRANGER: It's not a car. It's cattle. Herd of cows.

BILL: Course I've heard of cows. Hic! But you ain't driving 'em through here. Hic! This town only welcomes safe drivers.

STRANGER: Well?

BILL: Well, we ain't got a safe. Somebody just stole it.

STRANGER: I'm warning you, Sheriff. You'd better give permission or I'm going to drive my cows through here anyway . . . and I've got two thousand head.

BILL: Two thousand head? Hic! Why that's . . . 2,000 times 4 . . . that's 8,000 legs, divided by . . . Hic! Half that . . . hic! Take away the number you first thought of . . . Hic! That's . . . 2,000 cows!

STRANGER: Yep.

BILL: Well, look here, Stranger. I dunno whether you noticed, but I'm wearing two pistols.

STRANGER: Why is that?

BILL: In case one won't shoot far enough. Hic! All right? . . . Go for your gun.

STRANGER: O.K. Won't be long.

BILL: Stay there. Hic! I don't mean go for your gun, I mean draw.

STRANGER: Can't. I dun forgot my crayons.

BILL: That don't matter none. I'm gonna fill you so full of lead, every time you sit down you'll leave pencil marks. Hic! Now draw, you galloot.

STRANGER: But wait. I've got twenty-one children. All boys.

BILL: So I'm gonna shoot a twenty-one son galloot. [*Very angrily*] Draw, draw, draw! Hic!

STRANGER: Before you lose yer temper, Sheriff, I reckon you ought to know. I'm the fastest draw in the West. D'you still want to see me draw?

BILL: Hic!

STRANGER: O.K. . . . ready . . .
[*Sound effects: two bangs very loud and close together. Neither* BILL *nor the* STRANGER *has moved. The* SHERIFF *feels himself to see if he's been hit.*]

BILL: Phew! Well, Stranger, I never seen a thing. Just heard the two bangs as the gun went off.

STRANGER: I never actually fired the gun. The two bangs was my hands breaking the sound barrier.

BILL [*gulping nervously*]: Tell you what, Stranger, while yer cows is coming through here, let me buy you a drink at the saloon.

STRANGER: You wouldn't be scared would you, Sheriff?

BILL: Scared? No. I'm mighty grateful. I think you just cured my hiccups.
[*Music plays as they mosey off together.*]

CURTAIN

THE SOUTH DOWN HOUNDS

Cast of characters (in order of appearance):

DIANE BROWN — has a frightfully posh accent which makes 'South Down Hounds' sound like 'Sythe Dyne Hynds'

BRIAN RYAN — a round-looking, self-made man from Lancashire with an accent to match

MICHAEL MCLEOD — has a 'Hoots mon the noo' Scottish accent

This sketch explores the fun that can be had from three different accents. Some dog barking sound effects are needed off-stage. On-stage there is an easel with a sign which reads 'SOUTH DOWN HOUNDS — WE HAVE A WARM SPOT FOR COLD NOSES.'

[*Curtain opens.* BRIAN RYAN *enters left and* DIANE BROWN *enters right.*]

DIANE: Ah, welcome to South Down Hounds. So glad you found the road down. I'm Diane Brown, founder and owner of the South Down Hounds.

BRIAN [*blinking at her accent*]: How do. My name's Ryan. Brian Ryan from Ashton-under-Lyne.

DIANE [*blinking at his accent*]: Brian Ryan? How divine. Now then, Mr Ryan.

BRIAN: Oh, call me Brian, not Mr Ryan.

DIANE: Brian? Oh, fine. Well Brian, what did you have in mind?

BRIAN: I want a hound.

DIANE: Sorry?

BRIAN: A hound. A fierce hound.

DIANE: Oh, a hound. Well, your judgement was sound in coming to South Down Hounds to find a hound, even from Newcastle on Tyne.

BRIAN: Oh, quite. It was your advert I found in the *Ashton-under-Lyne Times* that brought you to mind. It said, 'At South Down Hounds you are bound to get more hound per pound.'

DIANE: More hound per pound. Yes, we find that it is due to advertising in the *Ashton-under-Lyne Times* and newspapers of that kind that South Down Hounds now abound in every town from Newcastle on Tyne, or Ashton-under-Lyne, right down to Sandown. Now, we know you require a hound.

BRIAN [*correcting her*]: A hound.

DIANE: But we don't know what kind of hound.

BRIAN: Cound of hound. Er – kind of hind – er – hound.

DIANE: Quite, quite. Fox hound? Bloodhound? Greyhound?

BRIAN: I thought a sort of brown hound.

DIANE: Brown? Oh, brine. A brine hind. Yes. Well, if we find our way to the hound compound, you will see the hounds bounding around the ground.

BRIAN: That sounds sound. Keeping the hounds in a compound.

DIANE: We do have the hounds' welfare in mind. Do bear in mind that some of our hounds are worth several thousand pounds.

BRIAN: How can a hound save up several thousand pounds?

DIANE: No, Mr Ryan. The hound does not own several thousand pounds. The price of the hound is several thousand pounds.

BRIAN: Price?

DIANE: But of course. We have one hound – an Alpine hound or mountain hound – that was sent to climb a steep incline to try to find nine snowbound mountain climbers. We waited a long time and just before the sun went down, we heard his whine and the astounding hound came bounding down dragging behind the nine new-found mountain climbers all safe and sound.

BRIAN: What's his price?

DIANE: Two thousand pounds.

BRIAN: Two thousand pounds? Can he yodel?

DIANE: Mr Ryan, I can't find time to clown around. What kind of hind do you have in mind?

BRIAN: I want a ground hound. A baying hound to roam the ground of my estate home and astound any scoundrels from the town who are prowling around.

DIANE: Oh, a guard hound. Several immediately spring to mind. A pointer would be just divine.

BRIAN: A bottle of milk?

DIANE: A pointer is a gun dog. There's one in the compound. See him running round and round and round.

BRIAN: What is he? A revolver?

DIANE: Do you mind, Mr Ryan? He's going for ninety-five pounds.

BRIAN: Ninety-five pounds for a revolving hound?
[*Enter* MICHAEL MCLEOD *the Hound Keeper.*]

MICHAEL: Ye widna be sellin' ma favourite hoond in the whole compoond for ninety-five poond the noo, Mrs Broon?

BRIAN: Eh?

DIANE: This is our hound minder Michael McLeod. This is Mr Brian Ryan from . . .

BRIAN: . . . Ashton-under-Lyne. How d'you do!

MICHAEL: How'r you the noo! I'd sooner you choose another hoond than my favourite hoond that's going roond and roond in the compoond. Would'ne a hoond for a few less poonds suit you doon to the groond?

BRIAN: Well . . .

DIANE: I'm sure Mr Ryan would be inclined to find the revolving hound just divine for running round and round his private grounds. What are the bounds of your grounds, Mr Ryan?

BRIAN: Y'what, love?

DIANE: How great is your estate, mate – er – might I inquire?

BRIAN: Oh, it's a large estate.

MICHAEL: And the size of the grounds around which the hound would be allowed to bound, morning, night and noon?

BRIAN: Oh, five in front and nineteen behind.

DIANE: Is that acres or square miles?

BRIAN: Feet. Five feet and nineteen feet.

MICHAEL: That's nay as big as the compoond the hoonds are boonding aroond the noo.

DIANE: And that's your estate?

BRIAN: No, that's my garden . . . attached to the house on the estate.

DIANE [*cheered*]: On the estate?

BRIAN: Yes. The housing estate.
    [DIANE *looks shocked.*]

BRIAN: It's very nice, but we do get prowlers prowling around and I need a hound to growl and whine from time to time and protect Mrs Ryan.

DIANE [*now very suspicious*]: How much did you have in mind to spend on a hound, Mr Ryan?
    [BRIAN *sheepishly doesn't answer.*]

DIANE: A hundred pounds? . . . Fifty pounds?
    [BRIAN *shakes his head.*]

MICHAEL: You will'na get much of a Sooth Doon Hoond for under fifty poonds.

DIANE: How much, Mr Ryan?

BRIAN: Well, I've brought a . . . pound.

MICHAEL: A poond?

DIANE: A pound?

MICHAEL: A poond for a hoond?

DIANE: A South Down Hound for a pound?

BRIAN: Well, it wasn't so much as a ground hound. It was to keep in the house as company for my spouse.

DIANE [*suspiciously*]: Your spouse? In the house with your spouse?

MICHAEL: A spoose in the hoose? Is that like a moose?

BRIAN: No. My spouse! My wife.

MICHAEL: Oh, the wee lassie?
  [BRIAN *is jolted by this and starts to cry.*]

BRIAN: How did you know?

MICHAEL: How did I know what, the noo?

BRIAN: How did you know I call my wife . . . Lassie?

MICHAEL: I did'na know you called the lassie Lassie, laddie.

BRIAN: I always call my good lady Lassie. Boo Hoo!

DIANE: Please, Mr Ryan. Now why do you call your lady Lassie?

BRIAN [*tearfully*]: Because . . . she thinks she's a . . . hound. [*He breaks down.*]

MICHAEL: The man's broken doon because his wife thinks she's a hoond. Boo Hoo! [*He breaks down too.*]

DIANE: Try to stop crying, Mr Ryan. How long has your spouse believed in her mind that she was a hound?

BRIAN: Ever since she was . . . a puppy. Boo Hoo!

DIANE [*attempting a stiff upper lip*]: I don't want to be unkind, Mr Ryan, but it's time you stopped crying for if the hounds in the compound hear the sound of your crying, they'll start crying until . . . we're all crying [*She bursts into tears.*] . . . and all because your wife thinks she's a hound. Boo Hoo!

   [*Sound effects of dogs crying off-stage.*]

MICHAEL: Och, I canna stand the hoonds boo hooin'. Give the man the hoond that goes roond and roond for a poond and let him be going.

DIANE: I'd be out of my mind to give a South Down Hound away for a pound.

BRIAN: Boo Hoo!

DIANE: But I can't be unkind. Mr Ryan, give me the pound. [BRIAN *hands over a pound note.*] Take the hound from the compound, back to your spouse in Ashton-under-Lyne before I change my mind.

BRIAN: Oh, Miss Brown. You are so kind. I'll get the hound from the compound and be homeward bound . . . [*He continues talking gleefully to the audience as he moves away.*] to my wife in Ashton-under-Lyne who is really quite sound, and tell her that at South Down Hounds you really do get more hound per pound. Now where is that hound? [*Exit.*]

MICHAEL [*surprisingly cheerful*]: Well, Miss Brown, you got a poond
for the hoond that was a bit of a loon and kept running roond and
roond and baying at the moon and digging holes in the groond
and would have driven all the other hoonds roond the bend soon!

DIANE [*in a broad Cockney accent*]: 'Corse I 'ave. What do you think
I've been training that hound for? When he lets the hound alone,
it'll turn around and come back home and we'll have a pound for
the hound and still have the hound. And if Mr Ryan from
Ashton-under-Lyne won't let the hound out alone, the hound
will start baying at the moon and howling out of tune so much
that old Brian Ryan will bring the hound home and give us
twenty pounds to take the hound off his hands. And that's how
South Down Hounds always wins . . . hounds down.

CURTAIN

JUST NOT CRICKET

Cast of characters:

CLIVE
DEIDRE

[*Curtain opens.* CLIVE *is practising keeping a straight bat. Enter* DEIDRE.]

DEIDRE: Hello, Clive.

CLIVE: Oh, hello Deidre.

DEIDRE: Have you seen Rodney?

CLIVE: Yes. He's in at the moment. Can I speak to you, Deidre?

DEIDRE: Yes, when I've seen Rodney.

CLIVE: But you can't. He's in!

DEIDRE: Yes. I want to see him before he goes out.

CLIVE: No. He's already gone out. You see, he's in!

DEIDRE: Oh, Clive. How can he be out when he's in?

CLIVE: I don't think you understand, my dearest. He's gone out to be in. He'll be out there as long as he's in. He won't come in until he's out, unless we're all out in which case he'll come in without being out.

DEIDRE: Why are you being so evasive, Clive?

CLIVE: I'm not, Deidre. It's just that . . . that . . . I love you.

DEIDRE: Clive!

CLIVE: It's no good, Deidre. I'm batty over you. You've really hit me for six. My short square legs go all googly every time I see you. Pitch in with me, Deidre, and our lives will know no boundaries.

DEIDRE: But Clive. It's Rodney that I love.

CLIVE: I knew it. The bounder has pulled another stroke. He always could bowl a maiden over . . . with his flashy driving . . . he'll never be faithful to you, Deidre.

DEIDRE: Oh, Clive, that's not fair.

CLIVE: What? He's always playing the field. It's a wonder he hasn't been caught out. If he's not pinching one in the gully, he's tickling one round the corner.

DEIDRE: Clive, I won't let you speak of Rodney in that way. He's not like that.

CLIVE: What? He's always having a glance at long legs and short slips. He doesn't even keep score.

DEIDRE: It's no good, Clive. He's already declared his intentions.

CLIVE: You mean . . . you're going into partnership?

DEIDRE: I'm afraid so, Clive. I'm . . . sorry.

CLIVE: Ah well. That's me – the proverbial duck. Out of the game without scoring. I would have loved the chance to give you some extra cover. Still, if you're ever stumped, I'll bail you out.

DEIDRE: Oh Clive, you are sweet.

CLIVE: Well, I always try to keep a straight bat.
   [*Sound effects of cricket match:* 'OWZAT' *followed by crowd roaring and applause.*]

DEIDRE: What's that? What's happened?

CLIVE: It's Rodney. He's been . . . dismissed.

DEIDRE: But how? Why?

CLIVE: I think – yes. He was chasing a flighty one outside the off stump and he's been caught behind the wicket.

DEIDRE [*gasps under the shock*]: The swine. Couldn't he keep his mind on the game? Even out there, in front of all these people.

CLIVE: No, you don't understand.

DEIDRE: I think I understand all too well, Clive. All you've told me must be true. Long legs and short slips and tickling round the corner ... and now, he's been caught behind the wicket. [DEIDRE *almost faints, but steels herself.*] Clive, I'm sorry. I've been wrong. A fool. If you'll still have me, I'm yours.

CLIVE: Oh, Deidre darling!

DEIDRE: Oh, Clive.

CLIVE: Oh, darling. From now on it will be all L.B.W.s.

DEIDRE: Isn't that Leg Before Wicket?

CLIVE: No. It's you I Long to Be With, so Let's Be Wed and Life'll Be Wonderful.

DEIDRE: Oh, Clive. Kiss me, darling. [*She falls into his arms.*]

CLIVE: Oh, steady on old girl. I can't just now. It's my turn to bat. [*He drops her and goes out.*]

CURTAIN

FULL OF
EASTERN PROMISE

Cast of characters (in order of appearance):

SLAVE
QUEEN DIANA, THE SULTANA OF ABADANA
MAID
WASSI WAROO, THE WASSIER
IYAM, THE JAILER/PRINCE MUSSPI

The setting is an Arabian palace with lots of cushions covering a bench or chaise longue. Here, QUEEN DIANA, THE SULTANA OF ABADANA *reclines eating a bunch of grapes. She is attended by a* SLAVE *who has a large ostrich-feather fan. (This could be made of paper.) The* SLAVE *waves the fan continuously with one hand while in the other (or even attached to his leg) he has a large drumstick with which he bangs a huge gong. (Huge gongs are very rare and expensive, but you could make something that looks like a gong and have someone in the wings banging a cymbal close to a microphone for the effect.) Each time the gong is struck, everyone on stage vibrates until the noise dies down.*

[*The gong sounds. Curtain opens.*]

SLAVE: Hello. Cor, what a job this is. Standing here all day waving this fan. You see, I'm the chief wave slave. Every waft causes a draught so that makes me the chief draught wafter. On top of all that, I have to bong the gong so I'm chief gong bonger too. So there you are – chief wave slave, draught wafter and gong bonger . . . and all for her, Queen Diana, the Sultana of Abadana. She eats grapes all day, but she'd rather have a banana.

SULTANA: Oh, where is my son? My long lost son, Prince Musspi? He left the palace twenty years ago on his bike just to get some bananas, but he has never returned. I have been waiting here for twenty bananaless years.

SLAVE: I bring you grapes every day.

SULTANA: For that I am eternally grapefull.
[*The* SLAVE *bangs the gong. Sound effect of gong off-stage. The* SLAVE *and the* SULTANA *vibrate. The* SULTANA *has a grape dangling near her mouth which shakes about until the sound dies down and then she pops it in her mouth.*]

SULTANA: Oh, where is my son Musspi? Musspi must be somewhere.
[*The gong sounds. Enter* MAID. *She has a bare midriff and wiggles her tummy when she speaks. During the gong sounds she wriggles about like an eel.*]

MAID: Your Highness, Wassi the wassier is here.

SULTANA: Is he?

MAID: No, Wassi. Wassi Waroo, the wassier, he is here.

SULTANA: Yes, Wassi. Is he? I mean is Wassi here? The wassier. Is he here?
[*The gong sounds. Enter* WASSI. *He bows and scrapes and waves his hands all the time he is speaking. When the gong is sounded, he uses his arms to make his loose-fitting Arab-style clothes flap about.*]

MAID: Your Highness, this here is the wassier.

SULTANA: Is he?

WASSI: No, Wassi. I am Wassi Waroo.

SULTANA: Are you?

WASSI: No, Waroo. Wassi Waroo, the wassier . . . I am here. The famous wassier, Wassi Waroo, how do you do.
[*The gong sounds. Everyone trembles.*]

SULTANA: Tell me, Wassier, have you any news of my son, Prince Musspi, who left here twenty years ago on his bike?

WASSI: Your Highest Highness, I have consulted the sands of the desert in which all knowledge is writ . . .

SULTANA: What rot.

WASSI: Rot? 'Tis not rot. 'Tis right.

SULTANA: 'Tis right? That in the sands all knowledge is writ?

WASSI: Right.

SULTANA: Well then, who wrote what is writ?

WASSI: The spirits writ it.

MAID: It's not writ . . . it's wrote.

WASSI: The spirits wrote it.

SULTANA: Wrote what?

WASSI: Wrote what is writ.

SULTANA: What right load of rot.

WASSI: You cannot say what is writ is rot.

MAID: You should say what is written is rotten, right?

SULTANA: Do not talk wet. I can say what is writ is rot, or what is written is rotten, or even 'tis a right load of rot what is wrote.

MAID: Wrote?

WASSI: Wrote? [*Shakes his head.*]

SULTANA: Right. Wrote.

WASSI: What rot. What is written could be written as well as writ, but never wrote.

MAID: Right. You could have what is writ written rotten, or what is written writ rotten, but never what is writ rotten wrote.

WASSI: Or wrote rotten writ.

MAID: Or rotten wrote writing.

WASSI: Or writing wrote rotten.
  [*The* SULTANA *waves her arms. The gong sounds.*]

SULTANA: How dare you question whether I, the Sultana of Abadana, should say writ, rot, write, written, rotten, writing or wrote. Whatever I say is right, whether it be wrongly wrote or truly writ, you half-wit twits. Rote? . . . I mean, right?
  [*They bow. The gong sounds.*]

SULTANA: What I want to know is what you know about my son, Prince Musspi, who left here twenty years ago on his bike.

WASSI: Your Highness, in the sands I am sure I have seen certain sorts of signs which say that your son will be seen soon.

SULTANA: Can you be sure that these certain signs of my son that you have seen are certain?

MAID: What she means is, are you sure her son's signs seen in the sand are surely certain to signify him being seen soon?
  [*All three speak together.*]

WASSI: The signs I have seen seem to say for sure . . .

SULTANA: Are you sure the signs you say you have seen . . .

MAID: Are you certain that the signs in the sand you have seen . . .
   [*The gong sounds.*]

SULTANA: What do the signs say?

WASSI: 'Tis mysterious, but the signs in the sand seem to signify that your absent son will be seen to have survived by [*Pause.*] . . . the partial eclipse of the moon.

SULTANA: An eclipse of the moon. But when is the next eclipse due?

WASSI [*dejectedly*]: In sixty years' time.

SULTANA: What? Then you have failed to find my son.

WASSI: But I have tried.

SULTANA: The only thing you have tried is my patience. Until my son is found you shall be dung into a flungeon. I mean flung into a dungeon. Call my jailer. Have I got one?

MAID: Yes, Your Highness.

SULTANA: Then call him.
   [*Exit* MAID.]

SLAVE [*to the audience*]: This should be fun. The jailer's name is Iyam.
   [*The gong sounds. Enter* MAID.]

MAID [*announcing him*]: Iyam, the jailer.

SULTANA: Well, where are your keys?

MAID: No, he's outside.

SULTANA: Who is?

MAID: Iyam.

SULTANA: How can you be outside when you are in here?

MAID: I'm not outside. He is.

SULTANA: Who is?

WASSI: Iyam.

SULTANA: You are in here.

WASSI: The jailer is outside.

SULTANA: Is he?

WASSI⎫
MAID⎭ [*in unison*]: No. Iyam.

[*The gong sounds. Enter* JAILER. *He is wearing pantaloons with bicycle clips. He has a large bunch of keys which rattle when the gong is struck. He is a bit dim.*]

SULTANA: Who are you?

JAILER [*slowly*]: Iyam . . .

SULTANA: Go on.

WASSI: Iyam the jailer.

SULTANA: You are the prisoner.

JAILER: Is he?

SULTANA: No, Wassi. Wassi Waroo. Who are you?

JAILER: Iyam, the jailer.

SULTANA: Well, where have you been?

MAID: He was outside.

SULTANA: Was he?

MAID: No, Iyam.

SULTANA: Is he the jailer?

WASSI: Yes. Iyam.

SULTANA: You're Wassi.

JAILER: Is he?

SULTANA: No, Wassi. Who are you?

JAILER: Iyam, the jailer.

SULTANA: Is he?

WASSI ⎫
MAID ⎬ [*in unison*]: No! Iyam.
JAILER ⎭
   [*The gong sounds.*]

SULTANA: Oh, I feel dizzy. Right, *you* – lock *him* up and don't let him out till you see a partial eclipse of the moon.

WASSI [*drops to his knees grovelling*]: Oh, no. Don't lock me up. People will say, 'Wassi, Wassi! Oh, where is he?' Or, 'Wassi Waroo, where are you?'

SULTANA: Take him away.

WASSI: Wait.

JAILER: Ten stone four.

WASSI: No. Not weight, wait. What are these? [*Pointing to* JAILER*'s ankles.*]

JAILER: They're my bicycle clips.

WASSI [*rising to his feet*]: Then what was writ was not total rot, just wrongly writ.

SULTANA: Don't start that again.

WASSI: But Your Highness, don't you see? 'Tis the sign. 'Tis the sign.

SULTANA: What, the partial eclipse of the moon?

WASSI: No – the bicycle clips of your son.

SULTANA: Then he must be . . .

WASSI: Musspi.
   [*The gong sounds.*]

MAID: Iyam?

SULTANA: Not you, him. He was my son all the time.

MAID: Was he?

WASSI: No, Iyam.

JAILER: I am Iyam.

MAID
WASSI } [*in unison*]: No, Iyam!

JAILER: No, I am.

SULTANA: No. You were Iyam, but now you are Musspi and the owner of all the riches in this kingdom.

JAILER: I am? Then Iyam . . . must be . . . Musspi.
[*The gong sounds. The cast wobbles downstage and forms a line –* SLAVE, MAID, WASSI, SULTANA, IYAM.]

ALL [*in rhyme*]: We hope everyone has enjoyed all the fun
In our tale about Wassi Waroo.
And just in case you were a little confused,
We'll try to explain who was who.
[*Each character points at whoever they are talking about but looks either to the front or to the others.*]

MAID: Now Iyam, her son.

WASSI: No, you were the Maid.

SULTANA: Iyam's mother and Musspi's was me.

SLAVE: Yes, Iyam the jailer and Musspi the son,

JAILER: They were one and the same and both me.

SULTANA: Now he was the slave.

MAID: Oh, was he? I see.

WASSI: It was I who was Wassi, not you. [*Pointing to the slave.*]

SULTANA: Yes, he was the slave,

SLAVE: Yes, she was the Maid,

MAID: The Sultana was you . . .
  [*Slight pause.*]

ALL: Toodle-oo.
  [*The gong sounds.*]

CURTAIN

MIND
THE TRAINS

Cast of characters (in order of appearance):

TANNOY VOICE
BUSINESS MAN
PORTER
SALESLADY
GIRL TRAVELLER
WEIGHING MACHINE VOICE
ODD CHAP
IRISHMAN

The setting is a railway station platform. We can see a weighing machine, a news-stand-cum-buffet, station nameplates and a Tannoy speaker.

[*Curtain opens. An off-stage voice speaks for the* TANNOY. *The destinations are incredibly garbled while the other words are quite clear.*]

TANNOY: The train now standing at Platform Four is for Farnsbarns, Noswold and Shergapagasaga, calling at Noswosrospos, Cosrosplonkington and all stations to Smuckt.
    [*Enter* BUSINESS MAN *who approaches a* PORTER.]

BUSINESS MAN: I say, Porter, have you seen your level crossing? One gate is half open and the other gate is half closed.

PORTER: Yes, sir. We're half expecting a train. Tickets, please.
    [*The* BUSINESS MAN *produces his ticket. We have only seen the back of the* PORTER *so far. He turns round and we now see that he is wearing boxing gloves.*]

PORTER: Must punch your ticket. [*He takes the ticket in the palm of one glove and punches it with the other. Then he hands it back.*]

BUSINESS MAN: Thank you. Must get a paper. [*He moves to the news-stand and speaks sharply.*] Mirror, please.
[*The* SALESLADY *gives him a hand mirror. He takes it and then realizes what it is.*]

BUSINESS MAN: Is this the only mirror you have?

SALESLADY: Yus.
[*The* BUSINESS MAN *hands back the mirror.*]

BUSINESS MAN: Do you have a *Sun*?

SALESLADY: He's at school.

BUSINESS MAN: *Mail*?

SALESLADY: 'Course he is.

BUSINESS MAN: No . . . Do you have a *Mail*?

SALESLADY: Well, there's me husband.

BUSINESS MAN: O.K. *Telegraph*, please.

SALESLADY: The Post Office is just up the road.

BUSINESS MAN: *Express?*

SALESLADY: Be along in a minute.

BUSINESS MAN [*distinctly annoyed*]: *Guardian?*

SALESLADY: I dunno the guard's name.

BUSINESS MAN: Do you have *The Times?*

SALESLADY: The times is on the board. But you can't rely on them for trains. Why don't you read a paper while you're waiting?

BUSINESS MAN [*now very angry*]: I'd love to. What paper do you have?

SALESLADY: Oh, we have the *Mirror, Sun, Mail, Telegraph, Express, Guardian, Times* . . .

BUSINESS MAN [*hysterically*]: Well, any one you like.

SALESLADY: Oh, I don't like any of 'em. Which do you like?

BUSINESS MAN [*guessing*]: *Express?*

SALESLADY: We're waiting for it.

BUSINESS MAN: Well can I have any paper you've got?

SALESLADY: We haven't got any papers. They're coming on the Express.
   [*The* BUSINESS MAN *breaks down and sobs.*]

SALESLADY: Oh, hang on . . . we've got the late *Extra.*

BUSINESS MAN: I'll have that.
   [*She hands it to him. While fishing for money he notices the date.*]

BUSINESS MAN: This is four days old.

SALESLADY: I told you it was late. That's 50p.

BUSINESS MAN: It says 23p.

SALESLADY: I told you it was extra!

BUSINESS MAN: Bah! [*He pays and goes off.*]

TANNOY: The train now standing at Platform Three arrived bang on time. Will anyone witnessing this accident please report to the Station Master's Office immediately . . .

[*A* GIRL *with a case passes the* PORTER. *She puts the case down and starts to undo her clothing. The* PORTER *watches. When she gets to her skirt and blouse the* PORTER *raises his eyebrows and rushes to stop her.*]

PORTER: Excuse me, madam. You can't disrobe here.

GIRL: I was told to change here for Yarmouth.

PORTER: No, you change trains not clothes. You'll be catching the four o'clock from London.

GIRL: Oh, I see. What time did it leave London?

PORTER: Four o'clock.

GIRL: Oh, of course. How silly of me.

PORTER: And again at 4.02, and again at 4.04, and again at 4.06, and again at 4.08.

GIRL: Why?

PORTER: The guard got his braces caught in the buffers. It'll be here at 5.15.

GIRL: Oh good. Is it a stopping train?

PORTER: Well, it has to stop to let people get on and off.

GIRL: Oh, how silly.

PORTER: Mind you, it gets very full.

GIRL: Really?

PORTER: Yes. Last week it was so full the driver had to come on the bus.

ODD CHAP: 'Scuse me. Where's the weighing machine?

PORTER: It's just over there.
   [*The* GIRL *sees it and moves towards it.*]

ODD CHAP: That's not big enough.

PORTER: Not big enough? Why not?

ODD CHAP: You'd never get a whale on there.

PORTER: Oh, no. You wouldn't get a whale on th – A whale?

ODD CHAP: A whale. It's outside.

PORTER: What kind of whale? A killer whale?

ODD CHAP: Well, it nearly killed me carrying it here.

PORTER: You've been having a whale of a time. But why bring it here?

ODD CHAP: To get it weighed.

PORTER: Pardon?

ODD CHAP: Well, this is a Whale Weigh Station?

TANNOY: Will the man who left his dirty socks in a First Class carriage on the 2.15, please go to the Station Master's Office where he can have . . . the carriage.

[*The* GIRL *stands on the weighing machine and puts a penny in. It speaks to her.*]

WEIGHING MACHINE VOICE: You weigh 9 stone 7 lb., you are 5ft 6ins. and have blue eyes and brown hair and you are catching the 5.15 for Great Yarmouth.

GIRL: That's fantastic. I don't believe it. I must have another go. [*She repeats the performance.*] That's just amazing. [*She goes off looking for someone to tell.*]

[*The* BUSINESS MAN *is standing with a paper at the Buffet.*]

BUSINESS MAN: Coffee, please, and without cream.

SALESLADY: Sorry, we ain't got no cream. You'll have to have it without milk. That'll be 72p.

BUSINESS MAN: That's a terrible price for a cup of coffee.

SALESLADY: Well, it's terrible coffee. You coming to the party?

BUSINESS MAN: When?

SALESLADY: Tuesday. One of the sausage rolls is twelve on Tuesday.

[*The* PORTER *is approached by a man with an Irish accent pushing a trolley with a wheel missing.*]

IRISHMAN: 'Scuse me. Do you know where I can get a spare whale?

PORTER: There's a fella outside with one.

IRISHMAN: What size is it?

PORTER: I dunno. He couldn't weigh it. What size do you want it?

IRISHMAN: Oh, about that big. [*He indicates the size with his hands.*]

PORTER: You won't get a killer whale that big.

IRISHMAN: I don't want a killer whale. I want a spare whale for me trolley. [*Exit.*]

PORTER: Must have been the *Irish Mail*.

TANNOY: Will Porter Brown, who is sweeping Platform Two with Porter Green, please put Porter Green down and use a brush.
[GIRL *enters and finds a* PORTER.]

GIRL: Hey, this weighing machine is marvellous. Come and see.
[*She drags him to the machine and inserts a penny.*]

WEIGHING MACHINE VOICE: You still weigh 9 stone 7lb. You are still 5ft 6ins. and you still have blue eyes and brown hair, but through all this messing about you have missed the 5.15 for Great Yarmouth.

GIRL: Oh, no. I simply must catch that train. I simply must.

PORTER: Oh, must you? O.K. Come here then. [*He helps her down off the stage*.] Here, take this just in case. [*Hands her the suitcase*.] Now, if you run that way, fast enough, you should catch the 5.15 for Great Yarmouth.

GIRL: But what if I don't catch it?

PORTER: Don't worry. If you don't catch that one, the next one will catch you . . .
   -[*The* GIRL *runs off. We hear a train coming*.]

CURTAIN

HOPALONG THERE, HOPALONG

Cast of characters:

TEX, A COWBOY
HOPALONG, A COWBOY WITH A LIMP

TEX: Howdy Hopalong.

HOPALONG: Howdy.

TEX: How come they call you Hopalong, Hopalong?

HOPALONG: Well, I was once crossing the Pecos.

TEX: Why?

HOPALONG: Pecos it was in the way. When I came to this hacienda.

TEX: And has e end a the story?

HOPALONG: Oh, no it ain't. The boss said they could give me a bed for the night.

TEX: All you had to do was find a room to put it in.

HOPALONG: Yup. No. The bed was in a room. Trouble was, somebody had stolen the legs off it two weeks previous.

TEX: They'd been lying low for a fortnight?

HOPALONG: Well, that night I lay in bed with my six guns at the ready.

TEX: Three in each hand?

HOPALONG: One in each hand. A six gun is a repeater.

TEX: What's it fire? Radishes?

HOPALONG: Suddenly I heard a rustle.

TEX: Rustlers?

HOPALONG: And there at the end of the bed I saw a ghostly hand.

TEX: A cow hand?

HOPALONG: Cows don't have hands. They have hooves.

TEX: Do they have horns?

HOPALONG: Yes.

TEX [*making the sound of a horn*]: Perp, perp! Look out! There's one coming.

HOPALONG: I saw this ghostly hand at the end of the bed . . . so I raised my gun . . .
[TEX *urges him on expectantly.*]

HOPALONG: . . . took careful aim . . . and fired.

TEX: What did you hit?

HOPALONG: My big toe.

TEX: So long, Hopalong . . .

CURTAIN

THE PHANTOM SAUSAGE STEALER

Cast of characters (in order of appearance):

SERGEANT TREADHEAVY	a rotund policeman with delicate feet and a red nose
W.P.C. GOLIGHTLY	a bubbly policewoman trying hard to be efficient
DELIVERY BOY	a cheeky Cockney
INTERCOM VOICE	
MRS PUGH	frightfully lah-de-dah
VILLAIN	non-speaking role

When staging this sketch, I suggest that the sausages be kept up the villain's sleeves by elastic bands.

[*The setting is a police station. W.P.C.* GOLIGHTLY *is standing behind the counter combing her hair. The telephone rings and she answers it.*]

GOLIGHTLY: Hello, Nutty Street Police Station. W.P.C. Golightly speaking . . . Who? . . . Oh, Sergeant Treadheavy is in charge . . . Speak to him? No . . . er, yes. He's here . . . a-abouts.
[*She covers the mouthpiece with her hand and looks off. The phone flex is fully extended and she struggles to get a better view.*]
Oh, where is he? It's important. [*She speaks into the phone again.*] Hold on. He's just coming.
[*She gazes off-stage as if looking through a window and gives a running commentary on* SERGEANT TREADHEAVY's *arrival.*]
He's crossing the road. He's just coming. [*To herself.*] Come on . . . Over the zebra crossing and . . . oh, look out!
[*We hear a crash from the wings and shouts of, 'Oy, oy, oy!'*

SERGEANT TREADHEAVY *makes a dramatic entrance seated in the basket of a* DELIVERY BOY*'s bike. The* DELIVERY BOY *pulls up in front of the counter.*]

TREADHEAVY: Oy, oy, oy! Why don't you ring your bell?

BOY: Because you're sitting on it.

TREADHEAVY: Get me out! Get me out!
[GOLIGHTLY *puts the phone on the counter and tries to pull him out. The* BOY *also helps but to no avail. Suddenly the* BOY *gets an idea.* GOLIGHTLY *steadies the bike while the* BOY *lifts the back wheel so that the* SERGEANT *is slowly tilted forward. He comes out with his feet on the floor but stays in a doubled-up position.*]

BOY: Ha ha . . . a bent copper!

TREADHEAVY: Ooh, me back.

GOLIGHTLY: Can't you straighten up?

TREADHEAVY: No, it's me back, me back.
[GOLIGHTLY *tries to straighten him up, but the* BOY *again provides the solution.*]

BOY: Try this.
[*He pips the horn on the bike very loudly and the shock straightens up the* SERGEANT.]

TREADHEAVY: Ooh, that's better. Thank goodness. [*He turns to the* BOY.] Now then, my lad . . .

GOLIGHTLY: Sergeant, quickly – the telephone. It's Scotland Yard.

TREADHEAVY: No, that's our telephone. They've got their own.

GOLIGHTLY: No, they want to speak to you on it.

TREADHEAVY: Oh . . . eh? Scotland Yard? For me?
[*He picks up the phone. His helmet is askew and he inadvertently puts the ear-piece to his helmet.*]
Hello? Hello?
[*He realizes something is wrong. He puts the phone down, takes off his helmet with attention to the strap and places it over the phone. He looks round and now can't find the phone. He gets hold of the flex at the phone end and traces it to under his helmet. He then gets the handset through the strap and to his ear.*]
Hello. Yes. Who?
[*He looks overawed. He puts his helmet back on and salutes.*]
Yes, sir . . . Certainly, sir. Oh, I will, sir . . . Thank you, sir.
[*He salutes again and puts the phone down which pulls his helmet off. He replaces the handset, puts his helmet back on and walks back to the boy pulling the phone with him. He disentangles himself with* GOLIGHTLY*'s help, muttering 'Scotland Yard' to himself until he is ready to face the* BOY.]

TREADHEAVY: Now then, let's deal with you, my lad. Hitting a police sergeant – an important police sergeant – with a bicycle on a zebra crossing is a serious offence. What's your name?

BOY: I've an excuse.
[*The* SERGEANT *produces a pad and pencil and begins to write.*]

TREADHEAVY: Ivan . . . that's Russian, isn't it? E-X-C-U-S-E . . . excuse.

GOLIGHTLY: That's not his name. This is the butcher's delivery boy, Philip Steak. I'm sure he didn't mean any harm.

TREADHEAVY: Mean any harm? I was halfway across that zebra crossing and he hit me right between the stripes.

GOLIGHTLY [*apologetically to the* BOY]: That *is* serious.

BOY: Does it count if I hit him on a black square?

TREADHEAVY [*splutters*]: What? Where do you think you were going at that speed?

BOY: I was in a hurry to get to the police station.

TREADHEAVY: Police station? Oh, well that's different. You'd better be going. Show him the way, Golightly.

GOLIGHTLY: But he's here, Sergeant. This *is* the police station.

TREADHEAVY: Eh? Oh. Well, there you are then. There was no need for all that rush, was there? Now, what seems to be the trouble?

BOY: Somebody has taken my sausages.

GOLIGHTLY: Sausages? [*She turns with alarm to the* SERGEANT.]

TREADHEAVY: Sausages. [*He begins to write and then makes a sudden realization.*] Sausages? That's what the phone call was about. Scotland Yard [*he salutes and then glares at* GOLIGHTLY *till she salutes too*] said they are looking for a phantom sausage stealer. They believe he's in our area and . . . [*He turns to the* BOY.] it appears you've found him.

BOY: No, he found me . . . and my sausages. Then he lost me.

GOLIGHTLY: Did you get a good look at him?

BOY: Oh, yes. I chased him. He stole about five yards of sausages. [*He goes into a mumbled description with action to show five yards, the thickness of the sausages and how they were knotted. Meanwhile, the* SERGEANT *continues.*]

TREADHEAVY: Right, Golightly. Get on to the Pandas. It's not feeding time is it? [*He consults his watch.*] No. Get on to the Panda cars and tell 'em to look out for five yards of sausages . . . er . . . with a fella. Five yards. O.K.? [GOLIGHTLY *goes to the intercom microphone and fiddles with it.*]

BOY [*ends his mumbling*]: . . . five yards of sausages.

TREADHEAVY: Right, lad. Now give me a description.

BOY: Pardon?

TREADHEAVY: You know – size, colouring, etc.

BOY: Oh, well – very long, quite thin, er . . . pinkish colour . . . and knotted about every that much. [*He indicates about four inches with his finger and thumb.*]

TREADHEAVY [*exasperated*]: Not the sausages. The thief. What did he look like?

BOY: Let me think . . .

GOLIGHTLY: Calling all cars, calling all cars. Be on the look-out for a string of sausages, last seen running down the High Street. Description to follow. [*She turns to listen to the* BOY.]

BOY [*to the* SERGEANT]: Ah . . . short and thinnish.

GOLIGHTLY [*over intercom*]: They are short, thinnish sausages . . .

BOY: . . . with very big ears.

GOLIGHTLY [*repeats without expression*]: . . . with big ears. [*To herself.*] Big ears? Could be, I suppose. Walls have ears.

BOY: And wearing a mask.

GOLIGHTLY: And wearing a mask.

INTERCOM [*astonished*]: Sausages in masks?

GOLIGHTLY: Yes. You've heard of bangers 'n' mashks. [*She grins and nods, then realizes that she can't be right and frowns.*]

TREADHEAVY [*to* BOY]: Right. You get off down the High Street and see if you can find the man. Leave the rest to us.

BOY: Right. [*He wheels his bike towards the doors.*]

GOLIGHTLY: Well, what do we do now?

TREADHEAVY: Well, when it strikes one, I has my lunch. [*We hear a gong-like bong.*]

TREADHEAVY: There it is.

GOLIGHTLY: Wait a minute. It's only twenty past twelve.

TREADHEAVY: Then what was that we heard? [*They both lean over the counter and look off-stage. Enter* MRS PUGH

*dragging a villainous-looking character. He is dressed in a sloppy
sweater with very loose, dangly sleeves. Over his head is wedged a
saucepan.* MRS PUGH *leads him by the handle.*]

MRS PUGH: Hello. My name's Mrs Pugh. Oh, I *am* glad I've found
you. Look what I've found in one of my pans.

TREADHEAVY: What is it?

MRS PUGH: It's a man!

TREADHEAVY: A man? In a pan? You can't cook a man in a pan.
That must be against the law. I'll look it up in the book.

MRS PUGH: I'm not going to cook him. Ugh, no! I've just found him.
I opened my pantry and there he was.

TREADHEAVY: There who was?

MRS PUGH: He was.

TREADHEAVY: Well?

MRS PUGH: Well? Do something.

TREADHEAVY: What?

MRS PUGH: Get him out. I want to use the pan. I want to cook my
cabbage.

[GOLIGHTLY *is examining the head under the pan.*]

TREADHEAVY: If you want to get the pan off, that's the fire-brigade, but if you want to get his head out, that's the hospital. Hospital for heads. Fire-brigade for pans.

MRS PUGH: But . . . but I don't know who he is.

TREADHEAVY: Don't know who he is?

MRS PUGH: No. I just found him in my pan.

TREADHEAVY: Well, that's not trespassing because he hasn't put his foot in it. We'll try breaking and entering. [*He consults a large book and mutters.*] Breaking and entering a saucepan . . .

MRS PUGH: But I need my pan for my cabbage. What will I do if I can't do my cabbage?

TREADHEAVY: Couldn't you open a tin of peas?

GOLIGHTLY: I think you should help, Sergeant. His head's quite stuck.

TREADHEAVY: You should have added a knob of butter. My mother always used to add a knob of butter. You don't get things sticking in your pans with butter.

GOLIGHTLY [*knocks on the pan*]: Can you hear me? Don't worry. We'll soon get you out. You're at the police station.
[*The pan becomes agitated.*]

GOLIGHTLY: Oh, he's getting in a state. Don't worry. I'll hold your hand. Eeeeek!

TREADHEAVY: What's wrong?

GOLIGHTLY: It's his hand. It's all cold and clammy.
[*She drops his hand on the counter. It is five sausages.*]

TREADHEAVY: It looks a bit pale. Here – let me rub it for you. [*He takes the hand, and as he shakes it the sausages come down the sleeve.*] By Jove! The missing links!
[MRS PUGH *and* GOLIGHTLY *discover that the other arm is the same.*]

MRS PUGH: Ooh, it's horrible.

TREADHEAVY: Do you know, I bet this is our Phantom Sausage Stealer.

GOLIGHTLY: Quick, Sergeant. Get the handcuffs.
   [*The* SERGEANT *searches his pockets. The* VILLAIN *struggles and gets out of the pan. He has big false ears and a mask. He runs off with* TREADHEAVY *and* GOLIGHTLY *in pursuit.*]

MRS PUGH: It's my pan. It's my pan.
   [*There are shouts off-stage.* TREADHEAVY *and* GOLIGHTLY *run back across the stage followed by the* DELIVERY BOY *on his bike. This time the thief is in the basket. As they stop,* TREADHEAVY *and* GOLIGHTLY *tie his feet and hands with sausages. He complains so they push one in his mouth as a gag.*]

TREADHEAVY: That's the end of a knotty problem.
   [*A gong sounds off-stage.*]

TREADHEAVY: And there's the gong for lunchtime.

GOLIGHTLY: But it's only half past twelve.
   [*The gong continues. Enter* MRS PUGH *with the pan on her head.*]

TREADHEAVY: I've told you before. Fire-brigade or hospital – or open a tin of peas.
   [*Exit* MRS PUGH *with the pan still on her head. The others follow.*]

CURTAIN

THE SINS
OF CINDERELLA

Original TV cast:

NARRATOR	Bernard Cribbins
IVOR NOTION	Johnny Ball
UGLY SISTERS	Billy Dainty
FAIRY GODMOTHER	Sheila Steafel
CINDERELLA	Jan Hunt
GUS BROKEVEN, MANAGER	Tony Hart
ODD BOD	Carmen Munroe

The ODD BOD *part includes sound effects and is the busiest role in the sketch.*

This sketch was originally written for the 'Star Turn' series on BBC 1. The characters read their parts standing round a microphone and each wore a different wig or hat to show which role he or she was playing. Remember to tell the audience to look out for three deliberate mistakes.

NARRATOR: There's an old saying among Pantomime people, 'The show must go on', so not surprisingly, on the first night of *Cinderella* at the Gigglesborough Empire, Ivor Notion, who was playing Buttons, suddenly said . . .

IVOR: It can't go on. It can't go on.

NARRATOR: This outburst was followed by someone bursting in to Ivor's dressing room. It was a man wearing a large red wig and a dress.

UGLY SISTERS: What can't go on?

IVOR: This suit. It's two sizes too small.

UGLY SISTERS: Of course it's too small, but you'll have to wear it. The chap that was going to play Buttons is off sick and you're his stand-in.

IVOR: How can I be a stand-in in a suit I can't stand in . . . let alone walk in. My knees keep buckling up under me.

UGLY SISTERS: No wonder. Look. You've got both legs down one trouser.

IVOR: Ooh, so I have.

UGLY SISTERS: I shouldn't worry about your costume. It's a tatty pantomime anyway. Look at me playing the Ugly Sisters. How can I play two Ugly Sisters on my own?

FAIRY GODMOTHER: Should be easy for you. You're twice as ugly as anybody else.

NARRATOR: These words came from a very tatty-looking fairy who was standing in the doorway.

UGLY SISTERS: Ivor, this is our fairy godmother, although in that costume you look more like a fairy's grandmother.

FAIRY GODMOTHER: I know. Me wand has lost its lustre and me costume's all tattered and torn. I was trying to iron it last night in front of the fire when this spark flew out and I scorched my tights and burnt a hole in my tutu.

CINDERELLA [*in an affected voice*]: Never mind, sweety. No one will notice you. They'll all be too busy looking at me.

NARRATOR: They all turned to see a very pretty girl who was playing Cinderella.

FAIRY GODMOTHER: I don't think we've met, deary.

CINDERELLA: No? I'm Jan Starlet. Last year I was in *Jack and the Beanstalk*. For a moment I thought you were the girl who played the back end of the horse that Jack sold at the market . . . Ah, here comes Gus.

NARRATOR: Just at that moment along came the manager of the theatre, Mr Gus Brokeven.

GUS: Now, here I am. Everybody ready? Good. Cinders, you look wonderful. Wonderful. Now look, everybody. I've got a real pumpkin here for the transformation scene. So be careful with it. It's got to last the three weeks that the show is running. Now, any problems?

FAIRY GODMOTHER: *Aw Gus.* Try to do something about our costumes.

GUS: Sorry, my love. It's too late now. Time for the show to start. Good luck, everybody.

CINDERELLA: Oh Gus, darling. Could I have some new tights,

sweety? These tights are so baggy they look more like slacks. I had two extra pairs when I was in *Snow White and the Eleven Dwarves.*

GUS: But of course. For you anything, my dear. I'll get some out of the Box Office money. It's all in this bag. I'll just put it here by the side of the stage.

ODD BOD: Opening. Beginners please. Overture.
[*The* ODD BOD *now does the sound effects of an orchestra tuning up.*]

NARRATOR: At this point I should explain that the very talented and versatile [*name of performer*] will play all other parts in this extravaganza, including a full pit orchestra, the two donkeys which will pull the coach – we couldn't get ponies – the Prince Charming and . . . the clock striking twelve.
[*The* ODD BOD *is still tuning. We hear a drum roll and a crash of cymbals, followed by the tapping of a baton.*]

NARRATOR: Very good. And so the show commenced and everything went very well. The Ugly Sister went off to the ball on her own together and left Cinderella all alone by the fire. Then suddenly . . .

FAIRY GODMOTHER [*standing on points*]:
Cinders, your Fairy Godmother's here,
You know I would not fail,
In fact I'd have been here five minutes ago,
But I've got an ingrowing toenail.

But this pumpkin I'll change to a golden coach,
Your rags I'll turn to finery
So that Cinders, you shall go to the Ball,
As soon as we've changed the scenery . . .
[*Impatiently*] . . . As soon as we've changed the scenery.

ODD BOD: Oh, sorry. Switch.
[*The stage is darkened and the cast stoop and move around in one dark mass.*]

NARRATOR: Immediately the whole stage was plunged into darkness and as the cast pushed, pulled and bustled to change the scenery, Cinderella changed into her ball gown.

CINDERELLA: Ha. Call yourself a fairy? What happened to the blackout then?

FAIRY GODMOTHER: Well, I waved me wand.

IVOR: Yes, she did her best.

CINDERELLA: Ha. She wasn't half as good a fairy as I was in *Aladdin* two years ago, when I was Fairy of the Lamp.

UGLY SISTERS: Stop arguing, you lot. Help get the coach and these two donkeys on the stage.

ODD BOD: Hee haw. Hee haw.

IVOR: This scene change is supposed to be instantaneous.

UGLY SISTERS: Well some instances last longer than others. Here. Grab a donkey.

ODD BOD: Hee haw.

UGLY SISTERS: Get out of the way. Right, that's it. O.K. Lights.
   [*The lights go up.* IVOR, *the* FAIRY GODMOTHER *and the* UGLY SISTERS *have somehow swapped headgear in the mix-up.*]

NARRATOR: And so on went the lights again to . . .

UGLY SISTERS: Hang on, hang on.
   [*They all swap back.*]
   Right.

NARRATOR: And so on went the lights to reveal a beautiful coach and the audience went . . .

ODD BOD: Oooh, aaah.

NARRATOR: But Gus, the manager went . . .

GUS: Oh, blast! Look. Someone has stood in the pumpkin.

NARRATOR: And so they had. There in the middle of the pumpkin was a neat little footprint.

UGLY SISTERS: Somebody's put their foot in it.

NARRATOR: But still the show went on. Cinderella got to the ball and met the Prince and they sang and danced together until suddenly . . .

ODD BOD: Dong . . . [*then speaking almost to herself*] one.

NARRATOR: The clock began to strike twelve.

ODD BOD: Dong . . . two.

CINDERELLA: Oh, 'tis nearly twelve o'clock. Prince Charming, I must go.

ODD BOD: Dong . . . three. [*In a deep voice*] Oh, please Cinderella do not go . . . Dong . . . four.

GUS: Just a minute. Somebody has stolen the takings.

ODD BOD: Dong . . . five.

GUS: The money. It was here by the pumpkin.

ODD BOD: Dong . . . six.

UGLY SISTERS: They must have pinched it in the blackout.

ODD BOD: Dong . . . seven.

FAIRY GODMOTHER: Yes, but who could have done it?

ODD BOD: Dong . . . eight.

CINDERELLA: I must go now. Goodbye, dear prince.

ODD BOD: Dong . . . nine.

NARRATOR: And with that, Cinderella ran up the stairs, and a glass slipper fell from her foot.

ODD BOD: Dong . . . ten.

IVOR: That's it! That's it! I know who did it.

NARRATOR: Said Ivor Notion.

ODD BOD: Dong . . . eleven.

NARRATOR: And quickly Ivor bounded forward and grabbed Cinderella by the ankle.

ODD BOD: Dong . . . twelve.

IVOR: Gotcha.

ODD BOD: Dong . . . thirteen. Oops, sorry – too many.

CINDERELLA: Ouch! Oh, let go of my ankle.

UGLY SISTERS: He's only pulling your leg.

IVOR: This is no leg pull. Under her voluminous gown I think you will find concealed the missing money.

CINDERELLA: I never did it.

ALL: Oh, yes you did.

CINDERELLA: Oh, no I didn't.
[*The audience should be encouraged to join in with this.*]

NARRATOR [*interrupting*]: All right, all right. She did, so there. Carry on.

IVOR: Yes, you did and I know because you made three silly mistakes. [*To audience.*] Do you know what they were? [*The audience make suggestions.*] They were:
1. In *Jack and the Beanstalk* Jack sells a cow at the market, not a horse.
2. Snow White lived with seven dwarfs, not eleven.
3. Aladdin's lamp contained a genie, not a fairy.

GUS: Ivor Notion you're quite a hero, a veritable hero.

CINDERELLA: Oh no, he isn't.

UGLY SISTERS: Oh yes, he is.

CINDERELLA: Oh no, he isn't. Besides you've no proof I did it.

IVOR: Oh yes, I have.

NARRATOR: Said Ivor, picking up the pumpkin with the footprint in it.

IVOR: The guilty party stood in the pumpkin. So, Prince Charming, your line I think.

ODD BOD [*falsetto voice*]: Whosoever . . . [*She coughs and assumes a deep voice.*] Whosoever owns the foot that fits this pumpkin . . .

CINDERELLA: Oh no, you're not trying that on with me.

IVOR: No need to. When I grabbed your ankle I found these.

NARRATOR: Ivor held out his hand.

UGLY SISTERS: Ooh, whatever are they?

IVOR: Pumpkin pips. They were stuck between her toes.

ALL: Yeeeuuughk.

CURTAIN

THE Y T REVIEW

Here are four sketches linked together by a common theme. With musical bridges these sketches would make quite a substantial item within a review show.

SKETCH ONE:

YT?

Cast of characters:

A   person who hates tea

B
C   } people who like tea
D

[*A chorus sings the song 'Everything Stops for Tea' – or you could simply play the record. The action takes place in front of the curtains so that a rapid transition can be made to the second sketch. Enter* A *and* B *carrying caption cards.*]

A: Why do people stop for tea? It's horrible. I hate tea.

B: I beg your pardon?

A: I mean . . . why tea?

B: Y T? You're talking in capital letters.
      [A *holds up the first caption which has a letter A on it. From now on, each character holds up a caption to represent the line as it is spoken.*]

A: A?

B: Y T . . . C?

A: O R . . . I C. Y T.

B: S. T S OK, C?

A [*disagreeing*]: T S OK F U 1 T. I 8 T.
    [*Enter* C *with his caption cards.*]

C: LO. R U 2 OK?

A: A? V 2?

C: S . . . I Z U 2. R U OK?

B [*nods*]: S . . . [*Shakes his head.*] . . . N O. I M OK – E 888 (*eights*) T.

C: E 888 T?

A: S. I 8 T – OK?
    [D *enters and joins in the conversation.*]

D: LO, U 3. R U N D Q?

B: R V N D Q?

D: S. R U N D Q 4 T?

A [*spins round in annoyance*]: O, F U 1 2 Q 4 T, U Q 4 T. S I Z B4, I 8
    T, C? [*Exit.*]

D: S E OK?

B: S, E S OK. E 888 T. V R N D Q 4 T 4 V o T. [*He looks puzzled and
scratches his head.*] Sorry. V R N D Q 4 T 4 V o (*love*) T.

c: S. [*He points after* a.] E 888 T S E Z. [*Pause.*] Initially.

b [*shows the last caption*]: OK.
[*This is followed by a jumble of letters on the card with* ½ R T *at the bottom.* b *looks baffled.*]

c & d: What's all that about?

b [*trying to understand his caption*]: Oh, they are just letters.

c & d: Letters?

b: Yes. Come on . . . [*He turns to the audience.*] . . . letters ½ R T. T T F N.
[*Exit* b, c *and* d. *Enter* a.]

a: Why is it everyone likes tea except me? I think it's awful stuff. And look what it does to actors who drink it in TV commercials. It turns them into monkeys. [*He does a monkey impression.*] Ooh, ooh, ooh. I don't see the attraction in tea. All it is is a few dried leaves in hot water. It's too silly for words. Now if someone could think of an alternative they'd make a fortune. [*Exit.*]

CURTAIN

SKETCH TWO:

THE SORCERER'S TEA BREAK

Cast of characters:

SORCERER	bearded and dressed in flowing robes
APPRENTICE	young girl

[*The curtain opens on a sorcerer's workroom. You need a table with a large pot, a few small ones and a large spell book. (Is that how you spell book?) The* SORCERER *is reading from the book and popping things into the big pot.*]

SORCERER: Legs of frog . . . and hoof of hog . . . and beasty catched in the fog.

> [*The beasty almost escapes. The sorcerer catches it and drops it in the pot.*]

Add to the mixture one egg shell.

> [*He cracks an egg onto the table and drops the shell in the pot. He then looks puzzled and re-reads the book.*]

Add to that one egg, shelled!

> [*He scrapes the egg from the table with his hands and drops it in the pot. He then wipes his hands on his robes.*]

And that should serve you very well. There, that's my dinner ready for the oven. Heh, heh, heh.

> [*Enter* APPRENTICE *carrying a cup of tea, no saucer.*]

APPRENTICE: Here's your tea sir, see sir?

SORCERER: Ah, good, good. Where's the saucer?

APPRENTICE: Don't ask me, sir. You're the sorcerer here, sir.

SORCERER: Ah, so I am. [*He juggles with some saucers, finally dropping and smashing them.*] Ooops!

APPRENTICE: That's not sorcery. That's juggling.

SORCERER: Nonsense. Juggling with saucers is sorcery. It's only juggling if you juggle with jugs. But let's get on.

> [*The* SORCERER *stirs the tea with a quill pen.*]

SORCERER: Ah, there's nothing like a nice cup of tea. [*He drinks and his smile turns to a grimace.*] Aaagh! This is nothing like a nice cup of tea. Did you make this tea?

APPRENTICE: No sir, Mr Sorcerer, sir. I didn't make it, sir. I just added hot water, sir. It's made of leaves, sir. Tea leaves, sir, in a box, sir, from a shop, sir.

SORCERER: Somebody sold you a box full of leaves? Is that all?

APPRENTICE: Yes, sir, Mr Sorcerer, sir. Seems silly, sir, I should say, sir.

SORCERER: Silly it certainly is. We're not buying boxes of leaves. The streets are full of leaves. We'll start making our own tea . . . [*thoughtfully*] Only we won't call it tea.

APPRENTICE: Why, sir?

SORCERER: All right, we'll call it Y.

APPRENTICE: Why, sir?

SORCERER: Yes, Y. Now go out and collect all the leaves you can find.

APPRENTICE: Leaves, sir. Leave it to me, sir. I'll leave now, sir, to find the leaves, sir. By your leave, sir. [*Exit.*]

SORCERER: Oh, leave off. Heh, heh, heh . . . [*He rubs his hands together.*]
Now to prepare the evil brew
Into which the leave will gew.
Then we'll strain it, crush it, dry it,
Box it and let people buy it. Ha, ha, ha!
   [*He turns to a fresh page in the book which is very dusty. He reads and potters back and forth between the shelves and the book, selecting things at random and dropping them into the cauldron.*]
Ah, yes. Now . . .
Legs of cricket, ear of bat,
Touch of this, bit of that.
Old teddy bear – now what's that doing?
Oh, of course, it'll start it bruin.

Liquid fats of boar or bear,
Flea snatched freshly from the hair,
Cat guts from a tennis racket –
Imagine all this in a packet?

A little ink, now not a lot – oh! [*He drops in the whole bottle.*]
Drinking this they'll end up blotto.
Still, if people feel ill, either day or night,
The ink in Y will make them right.
   [*The* APPRENTICE *returns with a variety of leaves on two boards.*]

SORCERER: Hey, what have you got there?

APPRENTICE: By your leave, sir. Leaves, sir, would you believe, sir.
   [*The* SORCERER *examines the leaves and drops some in the cauldron and throws some away.*]

SORCERER: Leaves? What kind, eh? Dock leaves? Yes. Dandelion leaves? Yes. Lettuce leaves? Too good for 'em. [*He throws them over his shoulder.*] Leave them out. Wavy leaves?

APPRENTICE: From a beach tree, sir.

SORCERER: Mmmm. Burnt leaves?

APPRENTICE: From an ash tree, sir.

SORCERER: Is that all you could find?

APPRENTICE: And these, sir. [*She points to the two boards she carried the leaves on.*] Off the oak table in the dining-room.

SORCERER: Aha, oak leaves! Splendid. [*He drops them into the cauldron or breaks them up to fit, saying as he adds the last one . . .*] And one for the pot. Good. [*He stirs the cauldron with a ladle.*]
That should do for our special brew.
Now we'll stir it and try it out . . . on you.
    [*He surprises the* APPRENTICE *who drinks before she realizes what is happening. She smiles, holds it, contorts her face, falls asleep and drops to the floor.*]
Er hum, yes.
Quite a relaxing effect it seems.
Oh, of course, I forgot the sugar and cream.
But who cares what happens when you drink the stuff,

As long as they buy it, that's enough! Heh, heh, heh!
  [*He goes back to stirring and sings to the tune of 'Everything Stops for Tea'.*]
If you're sitting all alone or relaxing,
Or you're working in a noisy factor-eye,
Just set yourself free
When the clock strikes three,
'Cos everything stops for Y.

CURTAIN

SKETCH THREE:

A COMMERCIAL BREAK

Cast of characters:

GIRL	glamorous with a 'silky' voice
EXECUTIVE	suited and moustached with a 'plummy' voice
YOB	punk with appropriate accent
BOY	a non-speaking part. He appears in a nightgown

OFF-STAGE ANNOUNCEMENT: And now, a short commercial break.
  [*Enter* GIRL *in front of the curtains.*]

GIRL: Hi. Say, have you tried Y? Why Y is wonderful, and do you know why? Why Y is the in drink, that's why, and if you don't try Y you'll never know why. Bye. [*Exit.*]
  [*Enter* EXECUTIVE.]

EXECUTIVE: We at Y are all working very hard to bring you the finest drink possible. And that is Y. But why, you may ask. And why not, I say! Why? Why Y is superb, that's why Y . . . [*He gets lost.*] What? I mean why? Er . . . why Y? That's it; why Y? Why everyone who tries Y drinks Y. Why? . . . . Well, what else can you do with it? [*He walks off bemused.*]

    [*Enter* YOB.]

YOB: Y is guaranteed untouched by human hands. They kick it into the packets with their feet. [*Exit.*]

    [*Enter* GIRL.]

GIRL: Hi. Why not go to bed with Y? Why? Why not Y? Why Y makes a wonderful nightcap . . .

    [*A* BOY *crosses the stage wearing a nightgown and a cup and saucer on his head. The* GIRL *doesn't see him at first. When she does, she breaks up in laughter and goes off, giving the impression that she hadn't expected to see him. Enter* EXECUTIVE.]

EXECUTIVE: Hello, again. I want to tell you that we at Y aren't making any claims. We aren't making any promises. We aren't making any free offers. What we are making is – money! [*He throws notes into the air. Exit.*]

    [*Enter* YOB.]

YOB: Every morning when I wake up, the first thing I do is have a cup of Y. After that, the rest of the day doesn't seem too bad. Yuk! [*Exit.*]

    [*Enter* GIRL.]

GIRL: Hi, Y lovers. Do you know Y actually cures deafness. My Uncle George was deaf and last week he tried Y and guess what? This morning he heard from his sister in California. [*Exit.*]

    [*Enter* EXECUTIVE.]

EXECUTIVE: May I recommend Y at bedtimes? At the end of a tiring day, tuck yourself up with a nice cup of Y. I find it's best to drink it just before you go to sleep . . . otherwise you'll spill it down your pyjamas. [*Exit.*]
  [*Enter* YOB.]

YOB: I used to drink fifteen cups of tea a day, but it made me sick. Then I changed to Y. Now it only takes one cup . . . yuk! [*Exit.*]
  [*Enter* GIRL.]

GIRL: Hi there, Y lovers. You are Y lovers, aren't you? Why I'm sure you are Y lovers. Well, if you aren't we'd like to know why! Well, we wouldn't really like to know why . . . what I mean is . . . [*She looks from side to side.*] If you have a packet of Y and . . . you don't like it, don't worry. Think about us. We've got millions of them. Oh my, oh my, have we got Y. [*Exit holding her head in her hands.*]

CURTAIN

SKETCH FOUR:

SHOP AT TESBURY'S

Cast of characters:

OLD LADY

SHOP ASSISTANT

POSH LADY

POSH MAN
  wearing a deer stalker hat and carrying a rifle

ODD BOD

TWIT

SPARE CHAP

TANNOY VOICE

This sketch requires a simple supermarket set. A double-sided row of shelves runs straight up the middle of the stage leaving room for people to pass at both ends. Downstage there is a tub containing packets and a poster above which

*reads 'Special Offer! Y It's better than your average beverage'. Other
advertising signs are dotted about with such slogans as 'It's time you knew Y',
etc. Upstage right is a meat counter and upstage left, there is a vegetable
counter. The props required are two supermarket trolleys, two wire baskets,
and items of food as indicated in the script.*

[*Curtain opens. A* shop assistant *is putting the finishing touches to the Y
display. Enter* old lady *pushing a squeaky trolley. She can make this noise
like a ventriloquist and the squeak can be established as a running joke. She
runs into the back of the* assistant *nearly knocking him into the Y display.*]

old lady: Young man, I bought these pears here a week ago and
they're still as hard as iron.

assistant: Really? Give them to me and we'll change them.
   [*She hands them to him in a paper bag.*]
   My, they are hard. You go and choose some more.
   [*The* old lady *squeaks off and the* assistant *takes from the bag a
   tin of pears.*]
   No wonder – they're still in the tin.
   [*Enter* posh lady *who prods the* assistant *in the back and nearly
   knocks him into the Y pile.*]

posh lady: I'd like a pound of bacon.

assistant: Lean back?

posh lady [*leaning backwards*]: I'd like a pound of bacon.
   [*The* assistant *goes to the meat counter and looks for the bacon.*]

posh lady: Is that tongue fresh?

assistant: Fresh? It's got off the plate and licked me twice.
   [*He drops the bacon in her basket.*]

posh lady: No, I'll have a piece of haddock.

assistant: Finnon?

posh lady: No . . . thick 'un.
   [*Enter* posh man *wearing a deer stalker hat and carrying a rifle under
   his arm.*]

posh man: I say, have you any grouse?

ASSISTANT: Sorry, no. We have some veal and ham pie.

POSH MAN: How can I go home and tell my wife I've shot a veal and ham pie? Have you any wild duck?

ASSISTANT: No, but I could annoy a tame one for you!

POSH MAN: Bah!
[*He turns to leave and gets into trouble with the* OLD LADY *who narrowly misses him and the Y pile. She squeaks across to the meat counter.*]

OLD LADY: How much is a T-bone?

ASSISTANT: 15p, madam.

OLD LADY: That's very cheap for a T-bone.

ASSISTANT: It's another pound if you want meat on it.

OLD LADY: I want something cheap.

POSH LADY: He's got pigs' feet.

OLD LADY: How does he get his shoes on?

ASSISTANT: Your haddock, madam.

POSH LADY: Thank you. Oh, how can I stop fish from smelling?

ASSISTANT: Put clothes pegs on their noses. Next.
[POSH LADY *moves away. Enter* TWIT *pushing a trolley.*]

TWIT: Could I have a pork pie, please? And could you cut it up? I'll have it for my lunch.

ASSISTANT: Certainly, sir. Shall I cut it into four pieces or six pieces?

TWIT: Oh, cut it into four. I'll never eat six . . .
[*The* ASSISTANT *does a double-take.*]

OLD LADY: I think I'll have a small chicken.

ASSISTANT: Do you wanna pullet?

OLD LADY: No, I'll push it in me trolley. [*She pushes the trolley and squeaks up to the* TWIT.]

TWIT: Ooh, you have got a squeak. Here, swap with me.

OLD LADY: Oh, thank you, young man. You're very kind.
[*The* ASSISTANT *tries to hand over the pie and the chicken, but it gets very confused with the swapping of trolleys. He finally succeeds.*]

ASSISTANT: And here's your pullet. Now hoppit.
[OLD LADY *moves away squeaking loudly. The* TWIT *tries his trolley and hears no squeak. The* ASSISTANT *is intrigued and follows the* OLD LADY *to the vegetable counter. He bumps into the* POSH LADY *and nearly falls into the Y pile.*]

POSH LADY: Do you have any asparagus tips?

ASSISTANT: No, we don't sell cigarettes. We've got some spinach – very good for growing children.

POSH LADY: I don't want to grow children. I've only got a window box. Do you have any large potatoes?

ASSISTANT: Sorry, only small ones. All the large ones have been sent to Wiltshire.

POSH LADY: Wiltshire? Why?

ASSISTANT: Because they have Devizes for Chippenham.
[*The* OLD LADY *squeaks in and bumps into the* ASSISTANT.]

OLD LADY: I want some foil for this pullet I'm pushing.

ASSISTANT: Right. How long do you want it?

OLD LADY: Oh, I shall want to keep it.
[*The* ASSISTANT *grabs a roll of foil from the shelf and drops it in her trolley. She begins to squeak out but the* POSH LADY *stops her.*]

POSH LADY: Just a moment. [*She turns to the* ASSISTANT.] Have you any castor oil?

ASSISTANT: Castor oil? What for?

POSH LADY: For those castors.
[*The* ASSISTANT *grabs a bottle of castor oil from a shelf and hands it to the* POSH LADY. *She bends to oil the wheels while the* OLD LADY *looks on. Enter* ODD BOD.]

ODD BOD: Do you have any wine?

ASSISTANT: We have a new wine in. It's a cross between Muscatel and Hock.

ODD BOD: What's it called?

ASSISTANT: Muck.

ODD BOD: I was looking for the new drink imported from the Lebanon. It's made out of barley and water.

ASSISTANT: What's it called?

ODD BOD: Lebanon Barley Water. [*Exit.*]

POSH LADY [*to* OLD LADY]: There, that should stop you squeaking.

OLD LADY: Well, if you don't squeak you don't get to know people.
[*She exits squeaking across the stage. The* ASSISTANT *follows and nearly collides with the* TWIT *coming the other way.*]

TWIT: 'Scuse me, do you think I'll like these Puffo Flakes?

ASSISTANT: Oh, yes. Even your dog will like those. They taste like a postman's leg.

TWIT: Do they go snap, crackle, pop, snap, crackle, pop, snap, crackle, pop?

ASSISTANT: Not as well as you do.
[*They are interrupted by the* SPARE CHAP.]

SPARE CHAP: This College Pudding – which college is it?

ASSISTANT: Dunno. Should finish up Eton.
[*Exit* SPARE CHAP.]

TWIT: Will these flakes give me energy, do you think?

ASSISTANT: Oh, yes. Professional footballers eat them. Puffo for extra professional puff.

TWIT: So if I want stamina?

ASSISTANT: Puffo Flakes.

TWIT: And if I want muscles?

ASSISTANT: Puffo Flakes.

TWIT: What about footballers' big legs? [*He holds his thigh.*]

ASSISTANT: Puffo. Large economy thighs.

TWIT: And square shoulders?

ASSISTANT: Oh, yes. Eat the boxes as well.

TWIT: Oh, I can't wait to get the box open and try some.

ASSISTANT: Oh, there's no Puffo Flakes in the box.

TWIT: No Puffo Flakes in the box?

ASSISTANT: No, the box is full of free gifts. If you want the flakes you
   have to send off the top of the packet.
   [*Exit the* TWIT, *mesmerized. Enter* OLD LADY *pushing her trolley and
   squeaking. She begins hitting the* ASSISTANT *with her roll of foil which
   she has taken out of the box.*]

OLD LADY: You can't fool me with this faulty foil, you fool.

ASSISTANT: Faulty foil?

OLD LADY: This foil's too small to wrap this pullet I'm pushing. It's
only big enough for sausages.

ASSISTANT: Sausages?

OLD LADY: Sausages! [*She pulls a string of sausages out of the tube of
foil.*] And I don't want sausages and I don't want faulty foil. I just
want me pullet. And I don't want to push it. I'll carry it. Goodbye.
   [*She wraps the sausages round the* ASSISTANT's *neck and goes off,
   leaving her trolley, but to everyone's amazement she is still squeaking.*]

TANNOY: Announcing today's special offer – Y.

TWIT: What?

TANNOY: Y – the new wonder beverage. It's time you knew Y. So
   this is the last day of our special offer. Today only, a packet of Y
   costs only 75p. So why wait? Get your packet for 75p and get to
   know Y. Definitely the last day at 75p. Y.
   [*During this announcement the cast all rush in and make for the Y tub.
   They eagerly grab packets and stuff them into their baskets. The* OLD

LADY *hits everyone with her pullet. They all grab what they can and exit.*]

ASSISTANT [*standing by the vegetable counter*]: Did you see that? All that scramble for Y because it's the last day at 75p. Tomorrow it goes down to 62p. [*He leans on the vegetable counter. It collapses. He falls in a heap.* CURTAIN. *The curtain opens again. The cast reprise with the song and stop suddenly on 'Everything Stops for Y'.*]

CURTAIN

FLYING SAUCERS
HAVE LANDED

Cast of characters:

AGNES ⎫
BERYL ⎰ two old ladies

[AGNES *and* BERYL *are knitting and talking.*]

AGNES: Well, there I was, doing me sprouts and looking out of my kitchen window, when it just came down in the back garden.

BERYL: What? Your washing line?

AGNES: No . . . this flying saucer.

BERYL: Oh.

AGNES: Just behind my dustbin it was, and this green man gets out.

BERYL: What? Out of your dustbin?

AGNES: No. Out of the saucer.

BERYL: Oh.

AGNES: Anyway, he comes up to the back door and knocks.

BERYL: Washing powder, was it?

AGNES: What?

BERYL: Was he selling washing powder?

AGNES: No . . .

BERYL: Tide.

AGNES: What?

BERYL: I wash in Tide.

AGNES: Me too . . . It's too cold out tide. Anyway, he says, 'Me . . . space . . . Take me to your leader.'

BERYL: Bold.

AGNES: Well, he was . . . yes.

BERYL: No . . . I sometimes use Bold. [*She smoothes her skirt.*] I washed this in Bold.

AGNES: It's not very white.

BERYL: Started out green.

AGNES: Fancy.

BERYL: Plain green.

AGNES: He was green.

BERYL: Who was?

AGNES: The fella . . . the fella what got . . .

BERYL: . . . out of your dustbin?

AGNES: No . . . out of the saucer. He says, 'Me . . . space . . . take me to your leader.'

BERYL: Who did he mean?

AGNES: My Bert, I suppose. He knows a lot about space. He's a car park attendant, loves telling people where to go, but he was at work, so I says, 'Come in and have a cup of tea'.

BERYL: Yes.

AGNES: Yes. Well, he said 'No'. He said, 'We've come from a distant galaxy.'

BERYL: Ooh . . . I do like that.

AGNES: Like what?

BERYL: Galaxy. Free gift, was it? Ooh, it's lovely. All creamy, was it?

AGNES: No. He was greeny. All greeny. Said he'd come from Aldebra.

BERYL: That's up the motorway, isn't it?

AGNES: I dunno. I said, 'Come in and I'll pop the kettle on.'

BERYL: 'Course you did.

AGNES: 'Course I did. Well, as I turned to walk away, there was this blinding flash.

BERYL: Ooh, that's good too.

AGNES: What is?

BERYL: Flash. Cuts cleaning time in half.

AGNES: I know.

BERYL: I'm half thinking of getting some Flash.

AGNES: No . . . this flash come from this thing in his hand. Like a torch it was. Flash! I looked round and he'd burnt all the wallpaper off me dining-room wall. Clean as anything.

BERYL: Never did like that wallpaper.

AGNES: I know. All gone it was. Would have taken Bert a fortnight.

BERYL: I didn't know Flash was good for stripping wallpaper.

AGNES: No . . . Anyway, I turned round to say 'Thank you', you know, polite like, and there he was getting back in his saucer and whoosh . . . he was gone.

BERYL: Just like that?

AGNES: Just like that. Never touched his tea.

BERYL: Funny.

AGNES: I thought that. I thought that's funny. Then I thought perhaps they was told what we was told when we were kids.

BERYL: What's that?

AGNES: You know, they always told us, 'Whatever you do, never drink tea out of your saucer'.

BERYL: That's right. Manners, innit?

CURTAIN

MONSTROUS VET SKETCH

Cast of characters:

MR TIMKINS	a man with a snake basket
MRS POTTS	a Cockney lady with a large prop basket
'ANIMAL'	in prop basket
MR MUGGINS	
YVETTE	the vet's assistant
DR DIDALOT	the vet

The setting is a veterinary surgery waiting-room with several chairs, a pile of magazines on a table and a tall locker or cupboard in a corner. On the wall is a sign marked 'Surgery' with an arrow.

[Curtain opens. MR TIMKINS *is waiting. He has a snake basket with a lid on his lap. He is secretly making buzzing sounds and follows an imaginary fly with his eyes. Suddenly the flap of the basket pops up and the snake grabs the fly. The snake can be made from a sock and there should be a hole in the back of the basket to accommodate the man's arm. Enter* MRS POTTS *pushing or pulling a large prop basket which shakes and jerks and threatens to open. Muffled growls are emitted – from the basket, not the woman. Fluff and feathers are also expelled with the movement.]*

MRS POTTS [*to basket*]: Calm down, now. Calm down. We're there now so there's no point in grumbling. [*The basket jerks.*] Now then, now then. [*To* MR TIMKINS.] It's the only way I could get him here. He's damaged his trunk.

MR TIMKINS: His trunk? What is it? An elephant?

MRS POTTS: What? No! Ha, ha! Silly sausage. No, the trunk I bring him in – he's ruined it. So I had to get this basket for him. It's the only way I could get him here. He's not keen on this vet. [*The basket jerks.*]

MR TIMKINS: He does seem very ferocious.

MRS POTTS: Ferocious? Not him. He's practically 'armless. Does most of the damage with his feet. Still, he can't hop about so much in there. [*The basket jerks.*]

MR TIMKINS: Practically armless? Does most of the damage with his feet? Hops about? It's a kangaroo!

MRS POTTS: Kangaroo? Who?

MR TIMKINS: In there!

MRS POTTS: How dare you. [*The basket goes wild.*] There, you've hurt his feelings. There, there, my precious.

MR TIMKINS: Sorry.

MRS POTTS [*to the basket*]: All right, all right. Settle down. Here, have a magazine. [*She sticks a magazine into the basket.*]

MR TIMKINS: I say, that's clever. He can read?

MRS POTTS: Nah. He only looks at the pictures. [*The basket jerks, burps and the torn-up magazine comes out.*] He's seen that one already.
 [*Enter from the surgery* MR MUGGINS *with a cabbage on a lead.*]

MRS POTTS: Ooh, hello Mr Muggins!
 [MR MUGGINS *spins round, sees* MRS POTTS *and the basket and is petrified. The basket shakes and muffled growls are heard. To avoid it,* MR MUGGINS *crosses downstage in a panic. The snake pops its head out of its basket to see what's happening.*]

MR MUGGINS: Keep that monster away from me. Keep it away! Come on, Towser, come on. [*Exit.*]
 [*As the waiting-room calms down there is a short 'buzz' and the snake grabs a fly. They all ignore it.*]

MR TIMKINS: Was that a cabbage he had on that lead?

MRS POTTS: Yes. Mind you, he thinks it's a collie, silly man. [*To the basket.*] All right, now. He doesn't like Mr Muggins. Here, have a lump of sugar. [*She puts her hand in the basket. When she snatches it back, the sugar and her glove have gone.*] Naughty. Mustn't snatch. Mr Muggins complained about him galloping all over his allotment. Be quiet now. He's a little hoarse.

MR TIMKINS: Oh? That basket's a bit small for a horse.

MRS POTTS [*nonplussed*]: 'Course it is.
    [*Enter* YVETTE *from the surgery.*]

MRS POTTS: Ooh, hello. Who are you?

YVETTE [*with a marked French accent*]: I am Yvette.

MRS POTTS: Oh, has Dr Didalot left?

YVETTE: Dr Didalot? Non, he is the vet.

MRS POTTS: You said you were the vet.

YVETTE: Non, he is the vet. I am Yvette. Who is next?

MR TIMKINS: I am. But you're not the vet. [*He gets up.*]

MRS POTTS: She keeps saying she's the vet. [*The basket shakes.*] Yes, yes.

YVETTE: Non, I am the assisting.

MR TIMKINS: Ah, I'm Mr Timkins.

YVETTE: I am Yvette. [*The basket goes mad.*]

MRS POTTS: I don't care whether you're a vet or not a vet, but you're upsetting my little precious. Shut up, noisy hound!

YVETTE: Hound? Hound? Why is zee hound in zee basket? Does he not like leads?

MRS POTTS: Nah, he hates Leeds. He's a Manchester United supporter. [*A football scarf and rattle appear briefly from the lid of the basket.*] Well, you can tell.
    [*The* VET *pops his head out of the surgery door.*]

VET: Yvette, what seems to be keeping you? Oh, no! Not that monster again.

MRS POTTS: Ooh, Mr Didalot, you're still here!

VET: Go away, go away! Quick! Quickly! [*The basket goes mad.*] It's the monster.
    [*The* VET *backs up to the locker.*]

MRS POTTS: Doctor Didalot, don't be silly. Doctor? Doctor? [*In a sing-song voice.*] Doctor Didalot, who's being a silly billy, eh? [*The basket erupts.*] Shut up, you stupid beast, shut up!

YVETTE: Doctor?

VET: Ssshh, sssh!

YVETTE [*whispers*]: But this man is next.

MR TIMKINS: Yes, Doctor, it's my pet adder. [*The snake pops out.*]

VET: Ssh, sssh!

SNAKE: Ssss, ssss.

VET: Sssh!
    [*He grabs the snake with one hand and pushes it back into the basket. He*

withdraws his hand but the snake is holding onto his fingers. The action goes to and fro as the VET *tries to put the snake back and it won't let go. The* VET *finally gets free and slams the lid of the basket. He sucks his fingers.*]
Ouch, ouch, ouch!

MRS POTTS: Doctor Didalot? Look, it's only me and my precious. [*While speaking she is trying to keep the lid on the basket closed.*]

VET: Go away. I won't see you or your precious little monster. Once bitten, twice shy.

MRS POTTS: Oh, Doctor. He won't bite you. He hates raw meat. [*She goes to open the basket.*]

VET: I can't see him. I won't see him. [*He is on the verge of nervous collapse.*] He, ha, hoo . . . Last time he ate my stethoscope. He, ha, hoo! Yvette, get me a Bob Martins. I wasn't trained to cope with monsters.

MRS POTTS: Doctor Didalot. [*She is frantically trying to hold down the top of the basket.*] His manners are much better now. I've taught him to say grace before he bites the postman.

VET: Go away!
[YVETTE *has the requested pill. She opens his mouth, pops in the pill and holds his mouth closed, stroking his throat as though he were a dog.* MR TIMKINS *looks on. His snake pops up and follows the conversation. The* VET *now gets a cricket bat from the locker.*]

MR TIMKINS: A cricket bat? Steady on, Doctor.

VET: He, ha, hoo! Last time we had to use a tranquillizer gun . . . he, ha hoo, . . . on me!

MRS POTTS: Doctor Didalot, please see him this morning. He's a bit excited because the cat upset him.

VET: He shouldn't have ate it. [*He puts on a fencer's mask or a bee-keeper's hat.*] I wasn't trained for this sort of thing. I should be treating little bunnies and pussy cats. All right, Yvette, open up. [YVETTE *gingerly opens the basket. It is menacingly quiet.*]

MRS POTTS: Oh, Doctor Didalot, it's so good of you to see Precious.

He thinks the world of you really, you know. And I do. We wouldn't put you to any trouble for the world. He likes you and your fancy dress clothes.

[*The* DOCTOR, YVETTE *and* MR TIMKINS *ignore her and stare at the basket. The snake is also inquisitive and gets closer and closer. As* MRS POTTS *reaches the end of her chat, there is silence. Suddenly the snake's head is in the basket and there is a tug of war.*]

MRS POTTS: Let go, you naughty thing, you . . .

[MR TIMKINS *withdraws his arm from the sock and the fight stops. The snake hangs limp down the side of its basket.*]

MRS POTTS: Ooh, I didn't think he liked snakes.

VET: What did I tell you? A monster, a monster! All right, come on. Let's get it over with. What is it this time, eh? Last time it was fleas.

YVETTE: Fleas? Eeek! [*She leaps onto a chair.*]

VET: All over the place they were. I was hopping mad.

MRS POTTS: He hasn't got a single flea any more.

VET: Probably all married with large families.

MRS POTTS: Come on, my precious. [*She moves to open the basket.*]

MR TIMKINS: No, no . . .

YVETTE: Non, non . . .

MRS POTTS: Don't be frightened. Come on. Let the doctor see.

MR TIMKINS: What is it? For heaven's sake, what is it?
[*The basket opens and up pops the grottiest schoolboy you have ever seen. He has toy hairy spiders on elastic hanging from his hands and arms.*]

BOY: This time I've got spiders, Doctor, but they're not eating proper. Look, this one is Billy, this one is . . . [*etc.*]
[*He jumps over and runs from one person to another dangling the spiders in their faces. There is chaos as the* VET *fends him off with the cricket bat.* YVETTE *climbs on the table and* MR TIMKINS *runs out.*]

MRS POTTS: Malcolm! Malcolm! Behave yourself. He's full of mischief, ain't he? The little devil.

CURTAIN

A RIGHT BONNY CHARLIE

Original TV cast:

NARRATOR	Graeme Garden
IVOR NOTION	Paul Daniels
BOATMAN, WEARING A WOOLLY HAT	Barry Cryer
HIGHLANDER, WEARING A TAM O'SHANTER AND A KILT	Lennie Bennett
AGNES, THE MAID, WEARING A MOB CAP	Maggie Philbin
FLORA MACDONALD, WEARING A TARTAN SHAWL	Toni Arthur
PRINCE CHARLIE, WEARING A BONNET COVERED BY A BLANKET	Stuart McGugan

This sketch was originally written for the 'Star Turn' series on BBC 1. The characters read their parts standing around a microphone and should each wear a different wig or hat to show which role they are playing. Remind the audience to look out for the villain's three mistakes.

NARRATOR: One May evening in 1746, somewhere on the coast of Scotland – about half way up on the left – a young English lad called Ivor Notion walked down to the quayside and accosted a weatherbeaten old boatman.

IVOR: Excuse me, boatman. How much to row across to the Isle of Skye?

BOATMAN [*with a Scots accent*]: Och well, let me see. You'll be English I'm thinking?

IVOR: You think very loud. I could hear that.

BOATMAN: Och aye. Well, the charge will be two pence to row across.

NARRATOR: So Ivor gave the man two pence and with a couple of pulls on the oars he was quickly away from the shore.

IVOR [*shouting*]: Hang on, I haven't got in yet.

BOATMAN [*shouting*]: Och, I didn't know you wanted to come with me. Passengers are sixpence extra.

IVOR: That's a lot of money.

BOATMAN: Aye, well. It doesn't do to be seen with an Englishman these days. Not since the Battle of Culloden.

IVOR: Oh, all right. Here's your sixpence. Now let me get aboard.

BOATMAN: Och, ye'll no be needing a board. The boat has seats to sit doon on.

NARRATOR: The boat arrived back at the quay, and as Ivor clambered in he stumbled over a greasy blanket in the bottom. He thought he heard a muffled groan from beneath it.

PRINCE CHARLIE [*covered with a blanket*]: Moan, moan.

NARRATOR: Then Ivor saw a figure approaching along the quay.

IVOR: Hang on. There's a lady wants a lift.

HIGHLANDER: Och, do ye mind, Jimmy. I'm no a lady, I'm a laddie.

BOATMAN [*to* IVOR]: Och aye. It's no a skirt. He's wearing a Highlander's kilt. Look. I'd prefer ye not to be English, for both our sakes. Do ye ken?

IVOR: Oh yes, I mean, Och aye, the noo, I ken right enough.

HIGHLANDER: Well, boatman. How much to cross to Skye?

BOATMAN: For a clansman like yerself? Why it's two pence.

HIGHLANDER
IVOR   } : Two pence?

BOATMAN: Och aye. There's a lot of water to be crossed.

HIGHLANDER: It does nae look a lot to me.

BOATMAN: Oh well, you're only looking at the top of it.

NARRATOR: That joke is a bit deep for me. Anyway, the boatman began to row and no one spoke until they were quite near the opposite shore.

HIGHLANDER: A penny for your thoughts, Boatman?

BOATMAN: Och, they're worth twice that amount. I was wondering when you'd be paying me your two pence for the fare.

HIGHLANDER: Och, ye know you can trust a Campbell. D'you see, in this kilt and sporran and all, I have nae pockets and nowhere to keep my purse. Perhaps this snivelling lad would lend me a few bawbees.

IVOR: Oh yes. I mean, Och aye. I'd like that – not a lot – but I'd like it.

HIGHLANDER: Och, yer a braw Scot. In fact, I would nae trouble you, but I'm desperate. There are British spies everywhere looking for Bonnie Prince Charlie.

PRINCE CHARLIE [*from under the blanket*]: Hurrump.

HIGHLANDER: Aye. I've been hiding for over a month in the Highlands, just outside Glasgow. I hope I'll be safer in Skye.

BOATMAN: Aye, ye will. Especially if you stay at Miss MacDonald's house.

IVOR: Och aye, he's right. I'm staying there. She's my cousin, Flora. [*He mouths it clearly.*]

BOATMAN }
HIGHLANDER } : Who?

IVOR [*repeats*]: Flora. I'll tack yez there and introduce yez the noo.

NARRATOR: Ivor was as good as his word and a great deal better than his accent. Within minutes he and the Highlander were at Flora MacDonald's door which was opened by the maid.

MAID: Well, if it isn't young Ivor. You'll be tired after your long journey.

IVOR: I've brought a Camel with me.

MAID: I thought you'd come from England, not Egypt.

HIGHLANDER: I'm a Campbell, not a camel.

MAID: Oh, I'm sorry. What fooled me was the hump in the back of your kilt. Now what do you want?

HIGHLANDER: I'd like to stay here for the night.

MAID: Och well, stay there . . .

NARRATOR: . . . said the maid, and she slammed the door in his face. The angered Highlander hammered on the door with his claymore and it was opened again to reveal a dour-looking young lady.

FLORA: My name is Flora MacDonald and I'm accustomed to people knocking with their hand and not one of those dirty great things.

HIGHLANDER: Aye well, in the Highlands I'm not accustomed to having the door slammed in my face.

FLORA: Ah well, there's a difference at MacDonald's. You'd better come in. Would you like some cold porridge?

HIGHLANDER: Och aye.

FLORA: Aye. Pity. It's hot at the moment. Still, make yourself at home while I fix you something.

NARRATOR: While Ivor and the Highlander laughed at the cold porridge joke, which was fairly new in 1746, Flora went to the kitchen where the maid was waiting for her.

MAID [*whispers*]: Psst, madam. There's someone at the back door.

FLORA: At this time of night? Who could it be?

MAID: Charles Edward Stuart.

FLORA: Och, I've no room for three of 'em.

MAID: No. Charles Edward Stuart – Boney Prince Charlie.

FLORA: You mean Bonny Prince Charlie?

MAID: Wait till you see his legs.

NARRATOR: And in through the door came a bedraggled-looking chap draped in a greasy blanket.

FLORA: Och, what a tatty-looking thing.

PRINCE CHARLIE: Aye, I found it in the bottom of the boat.

FLORA: I was referring to you, not the blanket. However could Prince Charles come to look so tired and weary?

PRINCE CHARLIE: It probably comes from waiting so long for my first line. Apart from that, I've been in hiding since Culloden. Weeks of wading through peat bogs and thistles in my kilt.

MAID
FLORA } : Ooh, nasty.

PRINCE CHARLIE: I was nearly caught in the Trossocks.

MAID
FLORA } : Mmm, fancy!

PRINCE CHARLIE: And at last I hid under the blanket in the boat hoping I would arrive in France.

FLORA: What? On the Isle of Skye ferry?

PRINCE CHARLIE: I'm called *Bonny* Prince Charlie, not Brainy. Will you help me to get to France?

FLORA: Aye, I will. But first you'll need a disguise. You can trust no one. Come upstairs with me. Agnes, you see that our guests get their porridge.

NARRATOR: While the Prince was being transformed, Agnes gave Ivor and the Highlander their porridge.

IVOR: Well, there's always something different about porridge in Scotland.

HIGHLANDER: Och aye. In the Highlands we practically live on it. That and haggis and tatties i' their jackets. But porridge like this here, that's my favourite. Would ye pass the sugar, please?

NARRATOR: The two ate hungrily until they were interrupted by a figure entering the room.

HIGHLANDER: Well, hello, madam. My name is Hamish. What's yours?

PRINCE CHARLIE [*wearing the blanket as a shawl to reveal his bonnet*]: Hello, I'm Charles . . . er . . . a char lady . . . er . . . a ladies' maid . . .

MAID: Er . . . she's Charlotte, the upstairs maid.

HIGHLANDER: What are you doing downstairs? Have you got the day off?

NARRATOR: Just at that moment . . .
[*Enter* FLORA.]

IVOR: Where are the flowers?

HIGHLANDER: What flowers?

IVOR: It says 'Inter Flora'?

HIGHLANDER: That says 'Enter Flora'.

IVOR: Oh, sorry.

FLORA: The maid is coming with me on an errand to the mainland. Ivor, would you go down to the quay and hold the boatman for me?

IVOR: I'd rather hold you for the boatman. Oh sorry – certainly, Flora.

HIGHLANDER: Hoots woman, are ye going the noo?

FLORA: Aye, the noo.

MAID: It's true, the noo.

CHARLIE: So we'll say toodle-oo, the noo.

BOATMAN: And that is the end of the noos.

HIGHLANDER: Och, ladies – ye must allow me to escort ye. With Sassenach soldiers everywhere, ye can trust no one.

CHARLIE: Least of all you, you saucy Scotsman.

NARRATOR: Flora could see there was no point in arguing so the party made their way down to the quayside, boarded the boat and headed for the other side.

HIGHLANDER: Are you warm enough, Charlotte dear?

CHARLIE: Och aye, and I'll thank you to keep your distance, you crafty clansman.

HIGHLANDER: But even from a distance – why you're as bonny as the purple heather.

MAID: Look, I can see English soldiers on the beach.

ALL: Where?

FLORA: Ssh, hold your huisht. It would only need a traitor among us now to give a shout and we'd all be under arrest.

BOATMAN: Under arrest? But for what?

IVOR: For harbouring Bonny Prince Charlie himself. Trouble is, we *have* a traitor here, in fact, a British spy.

FLORA: A spy? But who?

IVOR: Our friend here, the Campbell.

HIGHLANDER [*in an English accent*]: Are you referring to me? I mean [*reverting to a Scots accent*] d'ya mean maself? Why I'm as Scottish as an Angus steak.

IVOR: You may be as thick as an Angus steak, but you're no Scot because you made three typically Sassenach mistakes. [*To audience.*] Do you know what they were? [*The audience can make suggestions.*] They were:
    1. He said he had nowhere to keep his money but that is what a sporran is for.
    2. Glasgow is in the Lowlands, not the Highlands.
    3. No self-respecting Scot would put sugar on his porridge. He would always use salt.

HIGHLANDER: But hang on a second, Ivor. You're English yourself.

IVOR: Yes, so I am, but I do like to see fair play and you have been decidedly cheating.

HIGHLANDER: Confound you, sir. Take that . . .

NARRATOR: The Highlander rushed at Ivor, but our hero was too quick and sidestepped, sending the English spy over the side and into the water.

CAST: SPLASH.

MAID: Well done, Ivor.

FLORA: Och aye, you behaved just like a true clansman.

CHARLIE [*still in a lady's voice*]: Ivor Notion, you're a caution.

IVOR [*pinching the Prince's cheek*]: And you, Your Highness, you're a right bonny Charlie.

CURTAIN

CASH COWBOYS

Cast of characters:

HOPALONG, A COWBOY WITH A LIMP
TEX, A COWBOY

[*Enter* HOPALONG *followed by* TEX.]

TEX: Hold on there, stranger.

HOPALONG [*turns*]: You mean me, stranger?

TEX: Yep . . . Why, it's you Hopalong. Say, from the back you look like a perfect stranger.

HOPALONG: Is that so? Why, I wish I could come round the back and have a look.

TEX: Say, Hopalong, I ain't seen you since the last Indian uprising.

HOPALONG: You mean when Chief Sitting Bull sat on that cactus. Heh, heh, heh! Shucks. What you bin doin' since then?

TEX: Well, I been guarding Fort Laramie for five dollars a week.

HOPALONG: Five dollars a week? Heck, that ain't much to guard a fort.

TEX: Well it ain't the money, it's the fort that counts. Anyways, me being broke, I was wondering if you could lend me a little something.

HOPALONG: Well . . . I could lend you this. [*He hands him a cocoa tin lid.*]

TEX: Hey, this is tin.

HOPALONG: Shucks . . . I thought it was only five.

TEX: No. It's just a piece of tin. Ain't you got any paper money you could let me have?

HOPALONG: Well, I do have this here thirteen dollar bill. [*He hands it over.*] I got it off a saloon girl in Tucson.

TEX [*examining the note*]: Counterfeit?

HOPALONG: Yep, she had two.

TEX: Nope . . . I mean this note is counterfeit. They don't make thirteen dollar bills. You been twisted. What did you give her for it?

HOPALONG: A seven dollar bill and two threes. Say, what do you want this money for anyways?

TEX: I got to buy myself a horse.

HOPALONG: A horse? Gawdarn it. A horse like the one I got costs a lot of money.

TEX: How much did your horse cost?

HOPALONG: Dunno, I stole it . . . Say, how much was you thinking of borrowing?

TEX: Well, I reckoned about twenty dollars.

HOPALONG: Well, that's too bad, 'cos all I got is ten dollars.

TEX: Well, give me that fer now. [*He takes the note.*] That's O.K. Now you still owe me ten dollars.

HOPALONG: . . . Yep? . . .

TEX: And I owe you ten dollars.

HOPALONG: . . . Yep? . . .

TEX: So that means we're evens.

HOPALONG: Yep . . . Er, no! . . . Hang on there. That's a mighty odd way of getting evens. Say, what kind of a horse are you thinking of getting?

TEX: Well, I was counting on getting a Palomino.

HOPALONG: Well in that case you don't need the ten dollars.
 [*He grabs the note back again.*]

TEX: Hey! How come?

HOPALONG: Well, I'm a pal o' yours. Right?

TEX: Well, yep.

HOPALONG: Well, what I always say is: 'Any pal o' yours is a pal o'
 mino.' Hop on there, cowboy.
 [HOPALONG *turns and bends.* TEX *climbs on his back.*]

TEX: Well, O.K. Giddy up there, Hopalong.

HOPALONG: Easy on the spurs there, pardner . . .
 [*Exeunt. Clippety-clop music.*]

CURTAIN

ADVERBS

When I was a teenager, we played the adverb game on long journeys, making jokes like: ' "Ooh look, there's a lorry," he said truckulently'; or ' "Someone has stolen my chair," he shouted deseatfully'. Here is a whole sketch full of that kind of joke and, apart from the beginning, the whole thing can be read from the book, suitably disguised. The AUTHOR *needs to be quite well-spoken and serious, but* ANNIE *and* STELLA *may sound a little too clever unless they have accents. Cockney or country accents will make them and the whole sketch funnier. Note – the* AUTHOR *gets in the final joke.*

Cast of characters:

AUTHOR
ANNIE
STELLA

ANNIE: You're looking sad.

AUTHOR: Yes. I sent this short story to a magazine and they've sent it back and said that they don't like it.

STELLA: Aw, what's wrong with it?

AUTHOR: They said it doesn't live.

ANNIE: Aw . . . Look, you read it to us and we'll see if we can help.

AUTHOR: O.K.
    [*They all sit down,* ANNIE *and* STELLA *on either side of the* AUTHOR.]

AUTHOR: One night as I lay sleeping, I was awakened by a sound. I looked at my bedside clock. 'It's still the middle of the night,' I thought. Then I . . .

ANNIE: Just a minute. I can see what's wrong straight away. You've got no adverbs.

AUTHOR: What are adverbs?

ANNIE: Adverbs! Where's your grammar?

AUTHOR: She lives in Blimpton-on-Sea.

STELLA: No. Your English grammar.

ANNIE: Look. Your adverbs is your colour. Makes it live. I'll show you. [*She reads the script.*] One night as I lay sleeping *soundly* . . .

AUTHOR: But when I'm asleep I don't make any sound.

STELLA: Don't you snore?

AUTHOR: No!

STELLA: How do you know if you're asleep?

ANNIE: Look, all right. One night as I lay sleeping . . . dreamily . . .

STELLA: Or . . . deeply . . .

ANNIE: Yes. Any of those. They're adverbs. Make it live. Look, you read the story and we'll add the adverbs.

STELLA: And make it live.

ANNIE: And make it live.

AUTHOR: Oh, all right. One night, as I lay sleeping . . .

STELLA: Deeply . . .

ANNIE: Dreamily . . .

AUTHOR: . . . I was awakened . . .

ANNIE: Rousingly . . .

AUTHOR: . . . by a sound . . . [*He waits for an interruption but there is none.*] I looked at my bedside clock . . .

STELLA: Alarmingly . . .

AUTHOR: 'It's still the middle of the night,' I thought . . .

ANNIE: Darkly . . .

AUTHOR: Then I heard the sound again . . . 'It's coming from the top of the house,' I thought . . .

STELLA: Loftily . . .

ANNIE: No . . . roofully . . .
   [*They are beginning to enjoy it.*]

AUTHOR: I jumped up and looked through the window . . .

STELLA: With a glassy stare.

AUTHOR: And I saw a pair of legs. A man was hanging from the roof . . .

ANNIE: In great suspense.

AUTHOR: Suddenly, one of the dangling feet swung forward and kicked the window, breaking the glass . . .

ANNIE: Bootifully.

STELLA: No, painfully.

ANNIE: Painfully?

STELLA: The window pane!

ANNIE: Ooh yes. Go on.

AUTHOR: Then the man swung himself into the room and landed on the carpet . . .

STELLA: Ruggedly.

ANNIE: In a pile.

AUTHOR: 'Put the light on,' he said,

STELLA: Brightly . . .

AUTHOR: I did so and he quickly drew the curtains,

ANNIE: In closing . . .

AUTHOR: 'Watch it, I've got a revolver,' he said,

STELLA: Spinning round . . .

ANNIE: Dizzily . . .

AUTHOR: 'And don't think they're not real bullets,'

STELLA: He said blankly.

AUTHOR: 'Where am I?' 'In my apartment,' I answered . . .

ANNIE: Flatly . . .

AUTHOR: 'Who are you?' 'I'm an escaped prisoner,' he said . . .

STELLA: With conviction.

AUTHOR: 'How did you get out?' I asked . . .

ANNIE: Freely.

AUTHOR: 'Easy,' he replied . . .

STELLA: Simply.

AUTHOR: 'I picked the lock of my cell' . . .

ANNIE: Pluckily,

AUTHOR: . . . crept up on the warder . . .

STELLA: Guardedly,

AUTHOR: . . . and hit him on the head . . .

ANNIE: Bashfully.

AUTHOR: Then I went up the wall . . .

STELLA: Like a lunatic.

AUTHOR: And just managed to reach the top with my fingers,' he said . . .

ANNIE: High handedly.

AUTHOR: 'Then I dropped down on the other side . . .

STELLA: Con-descendingly.

AUTHOR: Unfortunately, I hurt my ankle,' he said . . .

ANNIE: Limply.

AUTHOR: 'Shall I ring the Infirmary?' I asked . . .

STELLA: Patiently.

ANNIE: No . . . hospitably.

AUTHOR: 'I've already rung, but the line was busy,' he replied . . .

STELLA: With an engaging smile.

AUTHOR: 'I want you to help me to get to Scotland,' he said . . .

ANNIE: Jockularly.

AUTHOR: 'By stealing a boat . . .

ANNIE: Craftily,

AUTHOR: Or a lorry . . .

STELLA: Truckulently,

AUTHOR: Or smuggling me onto a fast train,' he said . . .

ANNIE: Expressively.

AUTHOR: 'Or you could hijack an aircraft,' I added . . .

STELLA: Plainly.

AUTHOR: 'And you could fly away . . .

ANNIE: Airily . . .

STELLA: Or escape by air, flightily.'

AUTHOR: 'But first, I need some food to take with me,' he said . . .

ANNIE: Provisionally.

AUTHOR: Quickly I cut some cheese sandwiches . . .

STELLA: Caerphilly,

AUTHOR: And added some ketchup . . .

ANNIE: Saucily,

AUTHOR: While he sat, looking on . . .

STELLA: Watchfully.

AUTHOR: 'I'll need some money' . . .

ANNIE: He sang, with a small change in note.

AUTHOR: 'All my money is in the bank,' I answered . . .

STELLA: With great interest.

AUTHOR: Just at that moment the door flew open and in burst a policeman . . .

ANNIE: Forcefully.

AUTHOR: 'I'm from the C.I.D.,' he said . . .

STELLA: Initially.

AUTHOR: 'Don't come any further,' said the man . . .

ANNIE: Woefully.

AUTHOR: 'He's aiming a gun at you,' I shouted . . .

STELLA: Pointedly.

AUTHOR: 'Don't be a fool,' said the detective . . .

ANNIE: Idiotically.

AUTHOR: 'Give me the gun,' he ordered . . .

STELLA: Disarmingly.

AUTHOR: It looked as though the man was going to shoot, so I quickly grabbed from the wall a heavy painting,

ANNIE: Artfully.

AUTHOR: And smashed it over the man's head. 'Ouch,' he said . . .

STELLA: With feeling.

ANNIE: 'I've been framed.'

AUTHOR: The man slowly slid off the chair . . .

STELLA: De-seatfully,

AUTHOR: And fell to the floor. 'He's not moving,' I said . . .

ANNIE: Shiftlessly.

AUTHOR: 'He's O.K. I've felt his pulse,' said the detective . . .

STELLA: In a serious vein.

AUTHOR: 'You realize that you'll get a reward?' he said . . .

ANNIE: Bountifully.

AUTHOR: 'Good. Now I'll be able to visit my grandma in Blimpton-on-Sea,' I said, as a last resort.

CURTAIN

SPLASH DOWN

Original TV cast:

NARRATOR	Bernard Cribbins
IVOR NOTION, WAITER	Richard Baker
IVOR NOSEFRIT, DETECTIVE	Kenneth Williams
ALI BICRACKER, NOSEFRIT'S INDIAN ASSISTANT	Kenneth Connor
LADY LOADALOOT	Angela Rippon
SHEILA RESTUM, NOSEFRIT'S SECOND ASSISTANT	Barbara Windsor
TALLBODY, BUTLER TO LADY LOADALOOT	Peter Woods

This sketch was originally written for the 'Star Turn' series on BBC 1. The characters read their parts standing round a microphone and should each wear or hold something to show which role they are playing. LADY LOADALOOT – *a tiara;* SHEILA RESTUM – *a swimsuit;* TALLBODY – *white gloves;* IVOR NOTION – *a waiter's jacket;* IVOR NOSEFRIT – *trilby hat;* ALI BICRACK-ER – *turban.*

NARRATOR: When Ivor Notion arrived at Moneybags Mansion, the country home of Lady Loadaloot, and opened the door, he didn't know what he was letting himself in for.

NOSEFRIT: Hello, what are you letting yourself in for?

NARRATOR: . . . asked a man with a strong-box who was eyeing Ivor suspiciously.

IVOR: Er, my name is Ivor Notion.

NOSEFRIT: Really? That's a coincidence. My name is Ivor too. Ivor Nosefrit, Principal of the Ivor Nosefrit Security Organization. Now, what are you doing here?

IVOR: The employment agency said I was to be a waiter.

NOSEFRIT: Right. Well you can wait here.

NARRATOR: At that moment, in swept the figure of Lady Loadaloot herself.

LADY L.: Ah, Mr Nosefrit. You've arrived.

NOSEFRIT: Yes, m'Lady. The tiara containing the Loadaloot Diamond is in this strong-box.

LADY L.: Oh, I do hope it is safe. The diamond is insured for two million pounds. If anyone should steal it . . .

NOSEFRIT: Never fear, m'Lady. It will only be on the premises until the end of tonight's ball. Then it will be returned to the bank vaults. Meanwhile, my staff are already carrying out security checks. Ali? Where are you?

NARRATOR: Immediately from the kitchen emerged Ali Bicracker, Ivor Nosefrit's Indian assistant.

ALI: I am here, Boss. I have checked the kitchen staff for okayness. The chef is now doing his excellent speciality. He rolls rice into balls and dips them in caramel. All very tasty. All very good.

NOSEFRIT: Never mind that. From now on you are to keep watch outside Her Ladyship's bedroom door. O.K.? Good.

LADY L.: Do you think the diamond will be safe in my bedroom, Mr Nosefrit?

NOSEFRIT: Of course. Ali will stop anyone getting in through the door, and they can't get in through the window because your balcony is situated right over the swimming pool, and there we have Miss Restum. [*He calls out.*] Miss Restum?

NARRATOR: In through the french windows stepped a very voluptuous girl, dressed in a very brief bikini.

SHEILA: Yes, chief?

NOSEFRIT: Ah yes. This is my other security assistant, Miss Sheila Restum. Nothing much gets past her.

SHEILA: No. I'm going to lie by the pool all day looking inconspicuous.

IVOR: I can't believe that.

LADY L.: No, really. That won't be necessary. I have my Butler. [*She calls out.*] Tallbody.

TALLBODY: You called, Madam?

LADY L.: Yes, Tallbody. I was trying to explain that you will be keeping watch over the swimming pool below my window.

TALLBODY: That is correct, Madam.

SHEILA: But I'm doing that. I've already inflated me lilo.

TALLBODY: I assure you, Madam, your presence is not required.

LADY L.: No. Tallbody is an excellent swimmer. He once held the world record in the 400 metres backstroke.

IVOR: Oh, really?

TALLBODY: Yes, sir. It was due to my exceptionally fast diving start. Will that be all, Madam?

LADY L.: Certainly, Tallbody.

NOSEFRIT: I think Miss Restum might stay by the pool as well, now that she has got all her equipment ready.

SHEILA: Ooh, goodie. I'll go and float on me lilo. Traa.

NOSEFRIT: And now perhaps, Madam, we can take the box up to your bedroom for safety's sake.

LADY L.: Certainly. Er, who, incidentally, is this?

IVOR: I'm a waiter, Ma'am.

LADY L.: Well, don't stand there waiting. Bring a bottle of champagne up to my bedroom, and a corkscrew. This way, Mr Nosefrit.

NARRATOR: Ivor nipped into the kitchen and found a waiter's jacket, a bottle of champagne, two glasses and a corkscrew, and a couple of minutes later he entered Lady Loadaloot's bedroom. He was just in time to see Her Ladyship putting the tiara back into the strong-box.

LADY L.: Don't you know you should knock before coming into a room? And take your tie out of those champagne glasses.

IVOR: Sorry, Ma'am.

LADY L.: Just put the tray down there and leave the corkscrew. *I'll* open the champagne later.

NOSEFRIT: Yes. If that's all satisfactory, I'll go and check everything else. [*To Ivor.*] You come with me.

NARRATOR: Leaving Ali Bicracker on guard outside the room, Nosefrit and Ivor went down to the swimming pool and a few minutes later, Ivor began serving drinks.

IVOR: Orange squash with no ice for you, Miss Restum?

SHEILA: Ooh, yes please. [*She makes a chinking noise.*] Just a minute. I didn't want any ice.

NARRATOR: Miss Restum handed the glass back to Ivor. There in the glass was what looked like a piece of ice, but in actual fact was . . . the Loadaloot Diamond.

IVOR [*to himself*]: But how on earth did that get in there?

SHEILA: Ooh, look. Me lilo's going down. It's got a puncture. I'm sinking.

NARRATOR: Ivor quickly stuffed the diamond in his pocket and helped Miss Restum off the sinking lilo and onto the side of the pool. He was just trying to work out where the diamond had come from when Lady Loadaloot arrived with Ali Bicracker.

LADY L.: Mr Nosefrit, I have just caught this person asleep outside my door.

ALI: I was not asleep. I was pretending to be asleep when you ran straight into me.

LADY L.: Pretending? Ha!

ALI: It is true. If a thief is seeing me asleep, he is tipeetoeing past me and I am catching him because I am not asleep.

LADY L.: You are either asleep or not asleep. We cannot afford capriciousness when a valuable diamond is at stake.

NOSEFRIT: Quite so, Madam. But while we are arguing, someone could be stealing the diamond at this very moment.

LADY L.: Nonsense. It would take five minutes to open that strong-box and at least three or four minutes to prise the diamond out of the tiara with the corkscrew. Still, I shall go and check. Oh, Tallbody. Could I have a word?

TALLBODY: Certainly, m'Lady.

NARRATOR: Lady Loadaloot whispered something to her butler and then she and Ali Bicracker went back into the house. Nosefrit looked around suspiciously. Ivor felt the diamond in his pocket. Tallbody stood motionless. Then suddenly . . .

   [LADY LOADALOOT *screams*.]

ALI: The diamond! She is gone!

NARRATOR: Nosefrit and Miss Restum ran into the house, followed by Ivor. Ivor then popped his head back outside just in time to see Tallbody jump fully clothed into the pool. Sp-la-sh! Ivor rushed upstairs and just caught the others as they entered the bedroom.

NOSEFRIT: All right, what's all this about?

ALI: The diamond, sir. She has gone, see? She has been prised out of the tiara.

NARRATOR: It was just then that Ivor Notion had a notion.

NOSEFRIT: Quick. We must search everyone.

IVOR: You would save a lot of time if you asked Tallbody. He seems to think he knows where the diamond is.

NARRATOR: Miss Restum popped onto the balcony and looked down at the pool.

SHEILA: Ooh, look at Tallbody. He's swimming around with his clothes on.

NOSEFRIT: He's what? Good heavens, he must be looking for the diamond.

NARRATOR: And without further ado, Nosefrit, Miss Restum and Ali Bicracker jumped off the balcony and straight into the pool. Sp-la-sh! Sp-la-sh! Sp-la-sh!

LADY L.: Just what is going on?

IVOR: Lady Loadaloot, I would have thought you knew. Apparently the thief dropped the diamond into the pool. Probably in trying to prise it out of the tiara, they flicked it over the balcony.

LADY L.: Well, they will find it now.

IVOR: Not down there, they won't, because I have it here.

LADY L.: The diamond! My diamond! Give it to me.

NARRATOR: Lady Loadaloot rushed forward and grabbed at the diamond, but Ivor sidestepped and her ladyship went straight into the pool. Sp-la-douche!
[*Enter* LADY LOADALOOT *very wet and bedraggled.*]

LADY L.: Quick everyone, look! He has the diamond.

IVOR: Yes, I have it, but you were the one who stole it, probably for the insurance money. You planned to drop it down to your butler to get rid of, but it accidentally flicked out, hit the lilo and bounced into Miss Restum's drink where I found it.

LADY L.: That's ridiculous.

IVOR: No, it's not. It's true and I can prove it because you made three very silly mistakes. [*To audience.*] Do you know what they were? [*The audience make suggestions.*] They were:
1. You don't use a diving start in the backstroke. You and Tallbody lied in order to get Tallbody by the pool.
2. You don't need a corkscrew to open champagne. You needed it to open the strong-box and prise out the diamond.
3. You said it would take three to four minutes to prise out the

diamond with a corkscrew. Only one person could have known that was the method the thief would use – and that was the thief herself. [*He preens.*]

NOSEFRIT: Ooh, you are clever, Ivor.

ALL: Isn't he clever? Ooh, he is clever! There's a clever Ivor!

NARRATOR: Ivor glowed with pride. [*Pause.*] Then quite suddenly, the balcony collapsed.

ALL: Sp-la-dosh!

CURTAIN